Jessica flushed angrily.

"I'm not interested in your opinion, Mr. Fury. Not about my personal life and certainly not about my desirability. I want only one thing from you. The truth about my husband's death!"

Luke leaned back. Finally he raised his eyes to hers—hard, flintlike eyes that bored into her.

"All right, Mrs. Trent," he said at last. "I'm going to give you the truth. And you're not going to like it...."

Rosemary Hammond grew up in California, but has since lived in several other states. Rosemary and her husband have traveled extensively throughout the United States, Mexico, the Caribbean and Canada, both with and without their two sons. She enjoys gardening, music and needlework, but her greatest pleasure has always been reading. She started writing romances because she enjoyed them, but also because the mechanics of fiction fascinated her and she thought it might be something she could do.

Promise
of Paradise
Rosemary Hammond

Harlequin Books

TORONTO • NEW YORK • LONDON
AMSTERDAM • PARIS • SYDNEY • HAMBURG
STOCKHOLM • ATHENS • TOKYO • MILAN
MADRID • WARSAW • BUDAPEST • AUCKLAND

ISBN 0-373-17344-X

PROMISE OF PARADISE

First North American Publication 1997.

Copyright © 1995 by Rosemary Hammond.

Printed in U.S.A.

CHAPTER ONE

JESSICA sat primly across from the heavy-set man in uniform, just as she had been taught from earliest childhood, spine straight against the back of the chair, neatly-shod feet tucked under it, legs together and bent slightly, the skirt of her dark blue linen suit decorously covering her knees.

Above the constant roar of the airplanes taking off and landing outside the tightly-shut window and the low hum of the air conditioner, she listened politely—*had* been listening for the past ten minutes—while the Commanding Officer of the Pensacola Naval Air Station explained to her once more why any further investigation into her husband's death would be fruitless.

"Yes," she said quietly when he'd finished. "I understand, Commander Perkins. You've made it quite clear, and I do appreciate the fact that it's been a month passed since the accident and you're hesitant to re-open the case." She leaned forward slightly, clutching the bone-colored leather bag tightly in her hands, and her calm voice took on a note of real urgency. "But, you see, I have to know what really happened."

"Well, yes, Mrs. Trent, I can sympathize with that, but..." He raised his hands in a helpless gesture and gave her a weak smile.

"But," she added with a wry twist of her mouth, "my father-in-law has *suggested*, let's say, for want of a better word, that it's best to let the entire matter drop. Isn't that the real reason?''

Commander Perkins shrugged. "I can only repeat what I've already told you. Several times,'' he added with a hard edge to his voice. "The matter has been investigated. The Navy is satisfied. Your husband's father, Senator Trent, is satisfied. Why not just leave it alone?''

"I can't do that,'' she said, her tone taking on an equally-determined note. "I might as well tell you that my father-in-law had nothing to do with my coming here. In fact, he doesn't even know about it.'' She leaned even farther forward, her gray eyes fixed on him with such intensity that she didn't even notice when her handbag slid off her lap and dropped to the floor. "But I must know. I—I have my own reasons. Personal reasons that have nothing to do with the family. I was Paul's wife, Commander Perkins. Doesn't that give me some rights, in spite of the Senator's wishes?''

Commander Perkins sighed heavily. He sat for a moment frowning down at his desktop, littered with papers and files, then rose to his feet and walked over to the window. He stood there for several moments rubbing his hand over the back of his neck.

Watching him intently, Jessica could almost sympathize with him. He seemed a pleasant enough man, balding, middle-aged, growing a slight paunch around the middle, but carrying his dark blue uniform well. He was probably somebody's husband, father, even grandfather, a kindly man.

She was well aware of the bind she'd put him in. Senator Trent carried a lot of weight on the important Congressional Armed Services Committee, and the Navy would turn itself inside out to accommodate his slightest wish. But she had to find out the real circumstances of Paul's death, and she intended to make the poor Commander's life a misery, if she had to, until she did.

Finally he turned around. He leaned back against the windowsill, crossed his arms over his rotund middle and gave her a grudging smile.

"You're a very persistent young woman, Mrs. Trent," he said at last. "But you have to understand my position."

"Oh, I do," she said. "I understand perfectly. And I'd like to assure you that I have no intention of making waves. If I do discover anything new, I promise you I won't even tell the Senator about it. I have no wish to stir up a hornet's nest or make trouble for anyone. I just want the truth."

"Then why..." he began, then broke off.

"As I told you, I have my own reasons."

"Well, I'll do what I can. Where are you staying?"

"At the Paradise Motel in Destin."

He nodded. "All right. I'll be in touch." He laughed when he saw the suspicious look on her face. "No, I'm not just fobbing you off again. I know by now it won't do any good. You'll just be back tomorrow."

She picked up her fallen handbag and rose to her feet, then allowed him to usher her toward the door. When he'd opened it for her, she turned to face him.

"Then I can expect to hear from you soon?"

"This afternoon. I promise."

"Thank you," she said, holding out her gloved hand.

After they'd shaken hands, she turned and walked away from him, her back straight, her shoulders squared, her head held high. The Commander stood looking after her, shaking his head, the expression on his face one of mingled exasperation and respect.

Half an hour later, Jessica was back in the bedroom of her cottage at the Paradise Motel, a new luxury complex right on the beach. She took off her blue suit, hung it carefully in the closet on its padded hanger, slipped off her bone-colored pumps and inserted the wooden shoe trees, went to the window in her lacy silk slip.

Through the tall palm trees that swayed in the April breeze, beyond the broad stretch of glistening white sand was the vast blue-green water of the Gulf of Mexico. Early spring was the loveliest time of year along the Gulf Coast of Florida, but Jessica hardly noticed the beautiful sight.

She was exhausted from the session with Commander Perkins, but exhilarated, too. It had gone quite well. She was finally going to get to the bottom of Paul's death.

As she raised her hand to adjust the blind, a spark of bright sunlight caught the glint of her wide gold wedding band, and a sudden flash of the day Paul had slipped it on her finger came to her.

Her wedding day! The huge church decorated with banks of flowers and ribbons, all of San Francisco society in attendance. The happiest day of her life. Paul had looked so handsome in his

Navy dress uniform, had gazed at her with such love in his eyes.

Her heart gave a sickening wrench. What had gone wrong? How could that gallant, dashing young Naval officer have changed so drastically? The drinking, the womanizing. When did it all start? Was it somehow her fault? Had she failed him?

Now he was dead. She'd been sorry, of course, when she'd received the news, but also secretly relieved. No more of his lies, no more pity from her friends, or worse, their satisfaction at her humiliation. Still, the hot tears sprang unbidden to her eyes at the waste of such a promising young life.

Heaving a deep sigh, she wiped her eyes and went over to the bed to lie down. She'd known from the moment they'd received the telegram informing them of his plane crash that there was more to it than the simple words of the wire made it seem.

That very night, her father-in-law had gone straight to the library of the huge Trent mansion and, she knew, made several private telephone calls, most likely to his high government sources. When he'd come back his face had been ashen, and she'd known that it wasn't just the fact of Paul's death that had put that look there.

Her suspicions were confirmed when he virtually refused to discuss the matter. She had begged him for more details, but he'd only brushed her off, just told her, as Commander Perkins had done, that he saw no reason not to accept the official findings. Paul was dead. Nothing would bring him back. And the sooner they all put it behind them the better.

She'd waited a month, then finally decided to come to the Naval Air Station in Pensacola herself, right to the source, the place where the crash had taken place.

After three days of being fobbed off with excuses and good reasons why she should let it rest, today the Commander had promised to help her. She'd won at last. She was gratified at that, but now that her suspicions were confirmed, there really *was* something to cover up, she couldn't help feeling a little frightened at what she might discover.

She was awakened by the ringing of the telephone beside her bed. She sat bolt upright and shook her head to clear the cobwebs. She must have dozed off. It rang again and she snatched up the receiver.

"Hello."

"Mrs. Trent, this is Commander Perkins. I've arranged to have you speak to the civilian expert who investigates all our air crashes here at the station."

"Thank you, Commander. That's very kind of you. When can I meet with him?"

"Would this afternoon be convenient?"

"Yes, of course. Shall I come to the station?"

"No. He'll come to you, if that's all right."

"I appreciate that. When shall I expect him?"

The Commander chuckled. "Well, he *said* four o'clock. But knowing Luke, it could be any time up until midnight. I'm sorry. It's the best I could do."

"I'll be here," she replied firmly. "Whenever he shows up."

After she hung up, she went into the bathroom to shower. As she dried off and dressed in a deceptively simple pale yellow cotton dress, she realized she'd forgotten to ask the Commander what this Luke person's last name was. It didn't matter. Nor did it matter when he came.

After dressing and combing out her shoulder-length black hair in her usual plain style, the ends turned up slightly, she went out on the lanai to wait for him. It was already half past three. She hadn't had any lunch that day, in fact hadn't had much appetite at all for the past two months, and now, suddenly, she felt hungry.

She called room service to deliver a sandwich and salad, and ordered extra coffee, a bottle of their best white wine and a brand of German beer she knew most men appreciated. She wanted to make a good impression on "Luke", needed him on her side.

After finishing her lunch, she sat at the umbrella-shaded table and watched the surf roll in, sipping coffee and gathering her wits together so that she could ask the right questions.

Finally, at four-thirty, she spotted a man coming down the paved path from the motel. He was quite tall, lean, dark-haired and broad-shouldered, in his shirt sleeves, a jacket slung over one shoulder, and he walked with the lithe grace of a panther. As he crossed over to her own private walkway, coming out of the shade of the main building into the bright sunlight for a few seconds, she noticed that the thick hair which had seemed almost black, now glinted with golden highlights where the sun struck it.

As he approached, she rose to her feet. "Mr..." She hesitated.

"Fury," he supplied. "Luke Fury."

"Thank you for coming, Mr. Fury," she said stiffly. "Won't you sit down?"

He nodded and sat in the deck chair next to hers, slumping back against it, his long legs sprawled out in front of him. As she took her own seat she glanced covertly at him. He looked very tired, rather harried, and extremely annoyed. A faint dark stubble covered the bony planes of his face, and there were little creases at the corners of his eyes, a startlingly deep liquid green.

"Would you care for something to drink, Mr. Fury?" she asked politely. "There's coffee, wine. Or beer, if you prefer."

"Yes," he said, sitting up straighter. "A beer sounds good."

She reached down into the ice chest and took out a bottle of the German beer, a cold pilsner glass, and set them down on the table. He reached in front of her for the bottle, twisted off the cap, then raised it to his mouth and took a long swallow. When he'd finished, he wiped the foam from his mouth on the back of his hand, then turned to her and gazed at her silently through hooded eyes.

"I hope you don't mind sitting outside," she said. "It's such a pleasant day that it seemed a shame to waste it indoors. The cottage is really quite nice, but..."

He set his bottle down hard on top of the table and leaned slightly toward her, his green eyes like marble. "Listen, Mrs. Trent, let's cut the chitchat, shall we, and get down to cases. I'm a busy man, and you might as well know I'm here under protest. I'm not in the Navy. I'm a civilian. I don't take orders from anyone.''

Although his abrupt little speech had shaken her, she met the penetrating gaze steadily. ''Then why are you here?'' she asked evenly.

He gave her a wicked grin that held a hint of approval, and shrugged. ''Partly as a favor for Commander Perkins. Partly out of curiosity. We peasants are always interested to see how the aristocracy lives.''

''Aristocracy?'' she asked, puzzled.

''Sure, you know. I've done my homework. You live with your husband's parents, a mansion in Hillsborough, probably the most affluent suburb of San Francisco. Your father-in-law is an important senator. You come from a wealthy old Boston family. A very impressive background, Mrs. Trent. How could I refuse?''

Something about the way he kept repeating her name, the rather sneering tone underlying the simple syllables, had begun to irritate her, not to mention the way he insisted on baiting her about her background. What she wanted to do was smack that sarcastic grin off his face, but years of training in correct behavior stopped the wayward thought almost before it had formed in her mind.

''I see,'' she said. ''Does that mean you would have refused to see me if I were plain Mary Smith, the shopkeeper's daughter? Who's the real snob here, Mr. Fury?''

The nasty grin faded slightly and the smug look of satisfaction vanished altogether. ''Touché, Mrs.

Trent," he murmured grudgingly. "You have a point."

"My father-in-law has nothing to do with this," she went on in a low earnest voice. "In fact, he doesn't even know I'm here. What's more, if he did, he'd be extremely displeased." She leaned a little closer. "Look, Mr. Fury, I know you're a busy man, but what I want to know shouldn't take long. And I'm sorry to take you out of your way. I offered to go back to the station to meet with you, but Commander Perkins made the decision for you to come to me."

"Oh, it's not out of the way. I'm staying here myself, as a matter of fact." He gestured toward her cottage. "Not in such luxurious accommodations, of course."

She sighed. "Well, be that as it may, since you're obviously not happy to be here at all, why don't you just tell me what I want to know, and then you can be rid of me."

"All right. Commander Perkins tells me you have some questions about your husband's plane crash."

"Yes, I do. He said you conducted the investigation."

He nodded. "That's right," he replied noncommittally, and took another long swallow of beer. "What do you want to know? Or, more to the point, *why* are you looking into it now? It happened over a month ago. Didn't your father-in-law get the official report? You must have seen it yourself."

"Yes, I saw it. But I've never been satisfied with it."

He quirked a heavy dark eyebrow at her. "Why not?"

She hesitated, not quite certain how to answer. He was turning out to be a difficult man to deal with, and clearly annoyed at pulling the onerous duty of soothing the widow's ruffled feathers.

"It's hard to explain," she replied at last. "It all happened so fast, the call from Commander Perkins, the funeral arrangements, and my father-in-law seemed so determined not to discuss it at all that I became convinced there had to be something he was trying to cover up. He doted on Paul, his only son, and I can understand why he would do that." She raised her chin. "But as Paul's widow, I think I have a right to know the truth."

As she spoke he had gradually turned away from her, and was now staring out at the incoming tide, his face blank, his eyes squinting against the lowering sun. He seemed to be mulling over something in his mind, and Jessica could only wait, her hands folded patiently in her lap, to hear what he had to tell her.

Finally he shifted his gaze back to her. "Everything I had to say about your husband's death was in my report to Commander Perkins. I have nothing more to add to it. I'm sorry." He rose abruptly to his feet, then bent over slightly, placing the palms of his hands flat on top of the table. "Now, if you'll excuse me, I've had a long day."

Crushed by his blunt refusal, she stared dismally down at his hands, large, competent-looking, a workman's hands, but well kept. He wore a complicated-looking chronometer watch on his left wrist, with a plain leather band, and his well-muscled forearms were covered with a mat of fine silky dark hairs.

He turned to go, but then, as though struck by a sudden thought, glanced back at her. "May I ask you a personal question?"

Slowly she raised her eyes to his. "You can always ask," she replied.

"Why didn't you come to your husband's funeral?"

She could feel the hot flush stealing over her face, and found she could no longer meet that steady green gaze. "I was ill," she said shortly.

He only nodded briefly, then grabbed his jacket from the back of the chair, hooked his thumb under the collar and slung it over his shoulder.

"Well, I'll be seeing you, Mrs. Trent," he said. "Sorry I couldn't be more help."

He turned swiftly on his heel and sauntered off away from her down the path, then into the main building of the motel. She didn't take her eyes off his tall retreating form once, but he never looked back.

For a long time after he'd disappeared from view, Jessica sat motionless in her chair, hardly stirring a muscle, gazing out at the slowly setting sun on the far distant horizon of the blue-green sea.

She had learned exactly nothing from Luke Fury. Nor, if she was any judge of character, was there any hope that she ever would. A hard man. Probably a ruthless one, and he clearly disliked her, or the woman he imagined her to be. There had been contempt in just about every syllable he'd uttered during their short conversation, the way he'd looked at her, the expression on his face.

And asking her why she hadn't gone to Paul's funeral. Perhaps she should have told him about the miscarriage, but she still found that painful subject hard to discuss. She'd been so hopeful that a child might make a difference in her marriage, so thrilled at the new life she was carrying within her. But when she'd told Paul his reaction had merely been one of annoyance. Then when the news came of his death, she'd lost it.

Finally, with a sigh, she got up and went back inside the cottage. In the bedroom she stood before the full-length mirror for a few moments studying her reflection.

This was the woman Luke Fury saw, slim, medium height, simply—and expensively—dressed in her yellow cotton. Every strand of dark hair was carefully in place, her subdued makeup flawless, her poised carriage and confident lift of her head the product of years of training.

But that was only the facade, the superficial image that had been imposed on her by her patrician mother, the society she'd been born into. Underneath was a mass of seething emotion seeking an outlet. She'd hoped marriage to Paul Trent would provide it, but that had fizzled out almost from the honeymoon, and in the end she'd simply buried the emotion and assumed the role she had been so carefully-groomed to play since early childhood.

What was she supposed to do now? Go back to the Trent mansion in San Francisco, or perhaps to her mother's house in Boston, take her place in society once again, play her part, probably end up marrying again, someone as shallow, superficial and distant as her dead husband?

Everything in her rebelled against that fate. Why not just stay on here a while longer? The Trents thought she was in Boston staying with her mother. All except Helen, Paul's sister, her only real friend in that artificial hothouse world she'd escaped.

On an impulse, she picked up the telephone on the table beside it and dialed the Trents' number. It was early evening. Helen would be home from her volunteer job at the hospital by now.

It was the housekeeper who answered. "Trent residence."

"Hello, Martha. This is Mrs. Paul speaking. Has Miss Helen come in yet?"

"Yes, Mrs. Paul. Would you like to speak to her?"

"Please."

In a moment, Helen's gruff, familiar voice came on the line. "Jessica? Is it really you? How are you making out? Enjoying the Florida sunshine? It's raining here."

Jessica had to laugh. Leave it to her sister-in-law to inundate her with questions before even saying hello. Ten years older than her brother Paul, she'd been more like a maiden aunt to Jessica since her marriage, and was the one person she trusted implicitly.

'Yes, Helen," she said. "It really is me. The Florida sunshine is great. I'm sorry about the rain. And so far I've come up against a blank wall. No one will tell me anything."

There was a short silence. "Now why is that, do you suppose?" Helen asked at last.

"I wish I knew. You tell me."

"Well, it does suggest that there really is something to hide, just as we suspected."

"Of course it does," Jessica replied. She told her about her interview with Commander Perkins, the talk with Luke Fury. "He's supposed to be the expert who investigated Paul's plane crash, but not only does he refuse to tell me anything, he's obviously taken a personal dislike to me."

"Well, it's apparently going to be more difficult than you imagined. What will you do now? Come home?"

"Not on your life," was the instant reply. "I'm going to stay here, at least for a while."

"Good for you. Enjoy the sunshine. Get a tan. Who knows? Your stubborn Mr. Fury might change his mind. Don't worry about the home front. I'll keep Father off your back for as long as you want to stay."

"Thanks, Helen. I knew I could count on you." She paused for a moment, then went on more slowly. "Helen, let's say I'm right and there is something they're covering up about Paul's death. Am I making a mistake to pursue it? Maybe we'd all be better off not knowing."

"My dear girl, only you can answer that question. However, knowing you, I doubt you'll ever rest until you learn the truth about anything, no matter how much it might hurt. But you have to make up your own mind. Afraid I can't help you there."

The weather continued balmy and mild. Jessica picked up a few paperbacks in one of the hotel shops and for the most part lazed around each day, sunning herself, reading, swimming in the clear blue-green surf. She was enjoying the resort atmosphere, the privacy, so removed from her everyday life.

She did manage to get in one long walk along the shoreline late each afternoon, the fine white sand squeaking under the soles of her sandals, and since it was a private beach, she usually had the place pretty much to herself. She would return, pleasantly tired, and with the first real appetite she'd had in months.

It was late on Sunday afternoon, three days after her abortive interview with Luke Fury, that she saw him again. He'd said he was staying in the hotel, and although she'd kept an eye out for him, so far hadn't even had a glimpse of him. Each day her determination to tackle him again grew stronger, but it would have to be a casual encounter. He'd only sidestep a direct request for another interview, probably flatly refuse.

That afternoon she was heading down to the beach for a swim, dressed in her modest black suit, and just as she came around a thick clump of oleander, blazing with bright red blossoms, she saw him. He was standing at the water's edge, his back toward her, wearing only a low-slung pair of dark trunks, his hands on his lean hips, his legs spread apart. For a moment, all she could do was stare.

The man had a spectacular physique, which had been well-hidden beneath the rather rumpled suit he'd worn the last time they'd met. His dark hair gleamed with golden highlights in the bright sunshine, and drops of water glistened on his broad, tanned and solidly-muscled back and shoulders.

He turned just then, and before she could look away, he spotted her. Gradually his eyes narrowed and a slow smile spread across his face as he started sauntering slowly toward her.

Although her first instinct was to run, she stood her ground, waiting for him until he stood before her. He stood there, legs apart, knuckles on his hips, his eyes sweeping insolently over her from head to toe. Although her whole body seemed to be going up in flame, Jessica didn't move a muscle.

"Well, hello, Mrs. Trent," he drawled, his voice elaborately polite. "Still here, I see. I thought you'd have gone home by now."

"Oh, no, Mr. Fury," she replied coolly. "I don't give up that easily."

His eyes widened momentarily, the condescending smile replaced by a frown of annoyance. "You don't mean to say you intend to persist in this wild-goose chase of yours."

"Yes," she replied simply. "I do mean to say just that."

He shrugged. "Suit yourself. I've done all I can to discourage you." Once again his eyes swept over her. "That's rather a fetching outfit for a recent widow to be sporting, wouldn't you say? But perhaps a black bathing suit is your set's idea of a mourning outfit."

Jessica longed to slap the smug look off his face, but instead managed to give him a tight smile. "And what set is that, Mr. Fury?"

He grinned and swept an arm in the air. "Oh, you know. The beautiful people. The rich and the famous. All the upper echelons of society."

She gave a harsh laugh. "Your misconceptions about my life-style are rather naive, wouldn't you say?" She narrowed her eyes at him. "And any criticism of what I do or what I wear is pretty ironic coming from a man who can't even give a straight answer to a simple question."

He glowered at her then, his face like thunder. "Are you calling me a liar, Mrs. Trent?" he bit out through clenched teeth.

She shrugged. "You said it, Mr. Fury. How else would you define a person who hides the truth? Perhaps in your 'set' that's considered gentlemanly behavior, but it certainly isn't in mine."

His lips curled in a sardonic smile. "And who ever said I was a gentleman?"

"Not me, Mr. Fury," she replied, returning his smile. "It most certainly wasn't me." She started to push past him. "Now, if you'll excuse me..."

He put a hand on her arm, holding her back. "Just a minute. I'm not through."

"Oh? Does that mean you're going to tell me what I want to know?"

"No!" was the abrupt reply. "It doesn't."

She nodded briefly. "Then we have nothing more to say to each other." His fingers seemed to be burning into her bare skin and she tried to shake free of his iron grip. "And would you please let go of my arm?"

He stared for a moment, as though unaware he was still holding her. Then he quickly dropped his hand from her arm as though he'd been burned.

Jessica turned and strode away from him and continued down to the surf without once looking back. Although she was confident she'd carried off the encounter with the poise that had been bred in her, her heart was thudding erratically and her hands still shaking.

There was something very disturbing about the man, even beyond the fact that he was withholding information from her she was determined to get, something that shook her profoundly, at a level of her being she'd never experienced before. He reminded her of some kind of predatory animal, a panther perhaps, but one whose ferocity was well-concealed beneath a highly-polished veneer, except when his hide was pierced and the anger lurking underneath broke through to the surface, as it had just now.

The one thought burning within her, amounting to a mania now, even a personal issue, was that she'd get the truth out of him somehow, sometime, if it killed her.

When she reached the shoreline, she spread her towel on the sand, and had just started heading toward the water when suddenly, from behind her, came the sound of a woman's low laughter.

Slowly, she turned her head. Luke was still standing there where she'd left him, and running toward him was a tall redheaded woman, wearing a minuscule pink bikini that barely concealed her more than adequate physical endowments. When she reached him, she flung herself into his open arms, and he lifted her up in the air.

Just as his dark head bent down to hers, Jessica came to her senses. She turned around and ran headlong into the surf.

CHAPTER TWO

LATER that night, alone in her cottage, Jessica's mind wandered back to that scene on the beach. Her cheeks still burned at the insolent way Luke Fury's eyes had swept over her in her bathing suit, his nasty comment about her mourning apparel. But when she caught herself wondering idly what it would be like to have him look at her the way he had the redhead, she stopped herself short.

What she couldn't understand was why he seemed so hostile to her. He didn't even know her, yet every time they met he seemed to be accusing her of something. Somehow that last conversation with him only intensified her determination to get the truth out of him. It had become almost a personal issue between them now.

To do that, she'd have to stay on in Florida, which was what she wanted to do anyway. The thought of going back to the Trent mansion in Hillsborough or to her own parents' house in Boston chilled her to the bone. Somehow the loss of her child, Paul's death, the cover-up, had all brought about a gradual but dramatic change in her whole attitude toward her past life.

The idleness of it! The useless running around from one brilliant social affair to another, the dull people, the mindless gossip and backbiting. She wanted a taste of real life, where people worked for their living, made a difference in the world.

The only real problem in staying was money. The cottage at the Paradise was ruinously expensive. Although she'd been raised in luxury and lived her married life in similar circumstances, she actually had no money of her own, except for Paul's insurance. She'd always been given everything she wanted.

She sat down one evening to calculate exactly where she stood financially. When she'd finished, the prospect looked pretty bleak. The insurance money would carry her for several months, but then what? She really should spend as little of it as possible and bank the rest.

What she needed was a job. But what? She'd never worked a day in her life. Her expensive education at the exclusive women's college had taught her history, literature, philosophy, music and art appreciation, but not one practical skill. Was she even capable of doing anything that someone would pay for? Well, she'd just have to find out.

The very next day, she dressed carefully in her most businesslike outfit, a cream-colored linen suit, and drove back to the Naval Air Station at Pensacola. At the entrance to the Administration Building, she paused for a moment, took a deep breath, then marched inside, straight to Commander Perkins' office and asked his secretary if she could see him.

"Yes, of course, Mrs. Trent," the woman replied. "I'll just let him know you're here."

As Jessica thanked her and sat down in the visitor's chair, she had to smile to herself. For all her objections to her father-in-law's influence-peddling, his name did open doors for her.

Commander Perkins appeared at the door to his office in just a few minutes, a familiar suspicious look on his face. He obviously believed she was here to pester him again about Paul's crash.

"Mrs. Trent?" he said, ushering her inside his office and gesturing her into the chair opposite his desk. He seated himself then gave her another wary look. "What can I do for you today?"

"Well, first I wanted to thank you for arranging the meeting with Mr. Fury. He was most courteous."

A look of genuine amazement appeared on his broad bland features. "He was?"

She had to laugh. "You seem surprised."

"Well," he replied with a dry smile, "let's just say that with all his undoubted talents, tact is not one of them. He's tops in his field, the best there is, his services sought from all over the world, but he is inclined to be somewhat—ah—difficult when it comes to dealing with people."

But not all of them, she thought, recalling the sexy redhead. "Of course," she said aloud, "he didn't tell me anything new."

"Well, as I've tried to explain, there really isn't..."

She smiled at his obvious discomfiture. "Oh, don't worry. I'm not going to harass you about it again."

"Well, I'm glad to hear that." He half-rose out of his chair. "And thank you for coming to tell me. I assume you'll be going home, then. Is there anything else I can do for you before you leave?"

Might as well get straight to the point, she decided, taking a deep breath. "Actually I'm not leaving, but in order to stay, I'll have to earn some money." She leaned forward slightly. "I need a job, Commander Perkins, and I was hoping you might help me find something here on the base I could do."

For a moment he only stared blankly at her. "A job?" he asked at last. She nodded. Then he burst out laughing. "You're putting me on! Why would you need a job?"

"That doesn't really matter, does it?" she asked pleasantly. "The point is, can you help me?"

He leaned back in his swivel chair, steepled his fingers under his double chin and gazed out the window for several long moments. Jessica waited, cool as ice on the surface, in an agony of apprehension inside. What if he refused? Then what could she do?

"Well," he said at last. "Perhaps you'd better tell me what you're looking for. I mean," he went on with an embarrassed little laugh, "what are you trained to do?"

"Nothing, I'm afraid," she replied. "But I'm a quick learner, and I'm not fussy about what I do." She smiled. "I don't expect an executive position, or even a skilled job. Anything will do."

"Anything?" She nodded. He thought a few seconds, then said, "There is a position open in the base hospital for a cashier. Not very exciting, I'm afraid, but since you're not really trained and have no experience, I'm afraid it's the best I can do."

"That sounds great," she replied quickly. "Even I should be able to count money and make change."

He reached for a pen and pad of paper and scribbled a hasty message, then tore it off and handed it to her. "Here. Take this to the cafeteria manager. Her name is Millie Farrow. She'll fill you in on the details."

Jessica took the note from him and rose to her feet. "Thank you very much, Commander. I appreciate your help, and I'll try not to disgrace you."

Outside, she soon found the base hospital in the maze of grey-painted buildings, hard to miss actually, with the bright red cross painted on one side. The cafeteria was on the main level, and easily identifiable from the cooking aromas wafting from it into the hall.

Inside, she asked a waitress for Millie Farrow, and was directed to a harried-looking woman, about her own age, dressed in a white uniform and clearing off the tables. Jessica went over to her.

"Excuse me," she said. "I'm sorry to bother you, but I'm here about the cashier's job. Commander Perkins sent me." She held out the note he'd given her.

The woman looked up, pushed back the strands of blond hair that had fallen over her forehead and took the note. After scanning it briefly, she raised her eyes, flicked a brief glance over Jessica's obviously expensive suit, then nodded brusquely.

"Good," she said at last. "We could use the help." She named a salary. "When can you start?"

"Well, any time," Jessica replied. "I'll need a few days to find a place to live and get moved. How about Wednesday?"

"Great. Be here at seven o'clock." She stuck out a hand. "My name's Millie, Jessica. Welcome aboard."

* * *

That night she decided to splurge on one last dinner at the Paradise as a celebration for her success in finding a job. Tomorrow she would have to start looking for a cheaper place to live.

She was in the hotel dining room, enjoying a marvelous fresh halibut steak, when she saw him through the low bank of foliage plants that separated it from the cocktail lounge.

He was sitting at the bar, turned sideways and facing the same red-haired woman, who was now dressed in a green strapless sundress, cut low to reveal that perfect figure. He was leaning toward her, the same lazy smile curling on his lips, and the woman's hand was resting on his thigh.

Jessica turned her head quickly and began picking at her salad. The last thing she needed was a view of his seductive prowess in action. Although she had to admit the redhead was giving him every cooperation.

After a few moments, she dared to raise her eyes again, only to see that they were now walking directly toward her. She looked away hastily, but not before he'd recognized her, and when she glanced up again he was standing beside her table looking down at her, a half-amused, half-irritated expression on his face.

He also looked marvelous, a far cry from the rumpled man she'd first met. Freshly shaven, he was wearing a lightweight navy blue jacket, crisp white shirt and dark red tie, and was by far the most attractive man in the room.

"Well, good evening, Mrs. Trent," he drawled. "Still here, I see."

She raised her eyes and gave him a tight smile. "Yes," was the curt reply. Her eyes flicked to the redhead who was gazing at her with avid curiosity.

"Aren't you going to introduce me to your friend?" she pouted, giving Luke a nudge.

"Of course," he replied smoothly. "Sandra Forrest, this is Jessica Trent."

The two women murmured polite greetings.

Luke gazed lazily around the room, then smiled down at Sandra. "It's so crowded tonight I'm afraid we won't get a table soon. Might as well go back to the bar and have another drink."

Jessica started to get to her feet. "Here," she said, "I'm through. Take my table."

Luke glanced down at her half-finished plate. "Are you sure? We don't want to run you off."

"Oh, there's no danger of that, Mr. Fury," she replied in a saccharine voice. She turned to Sandra. "Nice to have met you," she murmured, then snatched up her handbag and beat a hasty retreat.

It wasn't until she reached the foyer that it dawned on her she'd neglected to pay her check. She stood there for a moment by the entrance in a quandary. What should she do? She really had no choice. She'd have to go back and get it.

With a deep sigh, she turned and started trudging slowly back to the table. With luck they'd be so engrossed in each other they wouldn't even notice. She could grab the check off the table where the waiter had left it, then make a quick getaway.

She had reached the bank of palms by now, and she stood there for a moment gathering up momentum, when suddenly from beyond the palm trees, she heard Sandra's voice speaking her name.

"So that was Paul Trent's wife. Why is she here?"

"To find the real story about Paul's death."

"And are you going to tell her?"

"I'd like to," came the grim reply. "Just to shake that icy composure of hers. But no," he added reluctantly. "I'm not going to tell her."

"Just because you're such a nice guy, I take it," Sandra retorted dryly.

"Something like that."

"Well, I feel sorry for the poor thing."

"Poor thing, my eye!" Luke exclaimed. "Why do you say that?"

"Oh, come off it, Luke. You know his reputation. He must have led her a merry chase."

Luke snorted. "Maybe she deserved it. From the stories I've heard, she's one of those socialite snobs who can't be bothered with a husband or children. A real cold fish."

"And just how would you know that?" Sandra gave a dry laugh. "Did you try and get slapped down?"

"Of course not. It was all over the base. Believe me, a man doesn't stray into another woman's bed, unless he can't find any comfort in his own."

"Oh, you men! You make me sick. Come on, let's order."

Jessica had stood frozen in place during the entire exchange, hardly able to believe her ears. So that was why Luke had treated her so cavalierly. It was so unfair! Had Paul spread lies about her simply to justify his own infidelities?

But it wasn't true! She'd loved Paul! He'd been everything to her, and it wasn't until her suspicions were confirmed, his wanderings become a matter of public knowledge, that she couldn't bear to have him touch her. She thought about the sleepless nights waiting for him to come home, the shattered hopes, the humiliation.

Now she had to get out of there. Bother the check. She could deal with that tomorrow. Her ears still ringing, she turned and fled.

Jessica spent the next few days apartment hunting. In that time she saw Luke several times, in the coffee shop, passing by in the hotel lobby, once in the parking lot as she was just coming in, he leaving. Each time he would nod politely, give her that same maddening half-smile, and always hurry past her.

Of course he was avoiding her, and it gave her a wicked sense of satisfaction that she had become such a thorn in his side. For now she would bide her time, wait for the right moment, then beard the lion in his den once again.

Then one morning when she went into the coffee shop for a late breakfast she saw him sitting by himself at a corner table, drinking a cup of coffee, a newspaper spread out before him. His back was toward her, but by now she'd recognize him anywhere.

Quickly, before he spotted her, she marched over to his table, pulled out the chair across from him and sat down. He glanced up, obviously startled, but by then it was too late for him to make his getaway. He frowned at her briefly, then folded up his newspaper, leaned back in his chair and gave her an exasperated look.

"All right," he said with a sigh. "What is it this time?"

She gave him a bright smile. "Oh, nothing new. The same old questions." Then her expression became grave. "I will get the truth," she said evenly. "All you have to do to get rid of me is tell me what I want to know."

"You know, Mrs. Trent," he said in a tone of deep irritation. "You're getting to be a real pest." Then suddenly, to her amazement, he put his elbows on the table, leaned toward her and gave her a slow smile. "But a very ladylike one, of course." The hooded green eyes swept her up and down insolently. "A very desirable one, too, if you could get the starch out of your spine long enough to act like a woman instead of a cog in your high and mighty social machine."

She flushed angrily, but wouldn't back down now that she had his attention. "I'm not interested in your opinion, Mr. Fury. Not about my social machine, as you call it, or my personal life, and certainly not about my desirability. You know nothing about me or my world. I only want one thing from you. The truth about my husband's death." Try as she might, she couldn't quite hide the catch in her throat or the quaver in her voice. "Can't you see? I won't be able to get on with my life until I learn that truth."

He leaned back again and sat there silently for several long moments, frowning down at his hands, flat on top of the table, as though deep in thought.

Finally he raised his eyes to hers again, hard, flintlike eyes that bored into her. "All right, Mrs.

Trent," he said at last. He rose abruptly out of his chair. "Let's go."

"Where?" she asked, looking up at him in alarm.

"To your cottage."

"But why?"

"I'm going to give you what you want. The truth. And I want you sitting down when I do because you're not going to like it."

Inside the cottage, Jessica lowered herself slowly into an easy chair, clasped her hands tightly in her lap and watched him as he ambled over to the small efficiency kitchen nook and got down on his haunches before the tiny fridge.

"Have you got anything to drink?" he asked.

"There's beer in there," she replied faintly, pointing. "And some wine." Her heart was pounding wildly, but with a lifetime of practice behind her, she managed to appear as calm and collected on the surface as ever.

When he came back, he had a bottle of beer for himself in one hand, a glass of wine in the other. He handed her the glass, then eased himself down in the chair opposite hers, popped open the beer and took a long swallow. Jessica sipped on her wine, still watching him carefully, wishing he'd quit fooling around and get to the point. He set the bottle down and leaned toward her, his elbows braced on his knees, broad shoulders hunched forward.

"I'm a plain-speaking man, Mrs. Trent," he began in a flat tone of voice. "Used to telling it how it is. You say you want the truth about your husband's death, and I'll have to give it to you in the only way I know how." He paused for a moment, the green eyes glittering at her, as though giving her a chance to back down.

"I understand," she said finally. "I want the truth."

"All right, then," he went on in the same brisk tone. "When your husband took up his plane that afternoon, he didn't clear it with anyone, as per regulations. He had no authorization. He was also drunk. That's a fact, the results of the autopsy." He leaned back in his chair, his eyes still upon her. "And he wasn't alone."

Jessica's eyes widened slightly, but she remained motionless. "I see," she said evenly. "Who was with him?"

He took another swallow of beer. "It was a woman," was the curt reply. Then his expression softened slightly. "Look, I'm sorry. I didn't want to tell you. There was no reason for you to ever know."

"Oh, don't waste your sympathy on me, Mr. Fury. I asked for it, after all. It's my responsibility, not yours." She thought a moment, then asked quietly, "And the—the woman with him?"

"Killed too," was the curt reply.

"My father-in-law knew, didn't he?"

"Yes. He did."

She took a deep breath and rose to her feet. "Well, thank you very much for giving me what I came here for. I know it couldn't have been easy for you. Now, if you'll excuse me, I think I'd like to be alone."

He stared hard at her for a moment, then got up from his chair, walked slowly toward her and stood gazing down at her. "Well," he said. "I'll have to hand it to you, Mrs. Trent. You've got guts." He cocked his head to one side and his mouth curled in a sardonic smile. "On the other hand, maybe you just don't really give a damn."

"You have no right to say that," she said in a low voice.

"Well, you'll have to admit that most women would have shown some sign of shock at news like that, even shed a tear or two." He eyed her carefully. "But then you're not like most women, are you?"

"I'm afraid I can't answer that," she replied. "I'm who I am. I don't know how to be anything else."

"Right." He nodded briskly then started toward the door. When he reached it, he turned around. "Sure you'll be all right?"

"Yes. Of course."

"Well, call on me if you need anything," he said. His tone was gruff, almost as though the offer embarrassed him.

"Thank you, but I don't think I'll need anything more from you."

He raised one heavy dark eyebrow. "You never know, Mrs. Trent. You just never know."

With that he was gone, and once she heard the door close behind him, his footsteps moving briskly away down the path, she was finally able to let go. Squeezing her eyes shut against the hot tears that stung behind them, her shoulders sagging, she groped her way back to her chair, sank down upon it and laid her head back.

She wasn't really surprised at the news Luke Fury had just given her, terrible as it was. She'd suspected something like that all along. It was one thing, however, to harbor dim suspicions, but quite another to have them confirmed. And by a complete stranger.

An enigmatic man, a conundrum. So curt and brisk, even rude, on the surface, yet there had been an unmistakable gleam of real sympathy in his eyes, those glowing green eyes, that seemed to conceal depths of emotion he didn't dare reveal.

She sighed deeply and opened her eyes, gazing around the room in sudden surprise, as though she'd wandered by mistake into a strange place. She pulled out a lacy handkerchief from the pocket of her dress, wiped her eyes, and blew her nose, promising herself that was the last tear she'd shed for any man.

By Tuesday she'd found an apartment in Pensacola she could afford, checked out of the motel, and packed her bags. She was just carrying the last of her luggage, the heaviest bag, down the path heading toward the parking lot, when she ran straight into Luke Fury.

Almost literally, since all her attention was focused on trying to balance the weight of the suitcase and still keep her footing in her high-heeled pumps, her eyes fixed firmly on her feet, and wishing she'd had the foresight to change into more sensible shoes before packing.

"Hey, whoa!"

She looked up to see him standing directly in front of her. One more step and they would have collided. At that moment her precarious hold on the bag slipped and it thudded to the pavement, barely missing her foot.

"Leaving?" he asked, picking up the bag easily and swinging around to walk beside her.

Although she was immensely relieved to be free of her burden, she didn't quite like the way he had simply taken over. "Yes, I am," she replied shortly.

"I'm sorry to hear that," he commented in a casual tone.

"Oh, really?" She gave a dry little laugh. "I must say that surprises me."

He grinned down at her. "I don't see why."

She shrugged. "Somehow I had the distinct impression you'd be overjoyed never to set eyes on me again after the way I hounded you."

"Oh, you couldn't be more wrong," he said in firm tones. "I never feel hounded when a beautiful woman pursues me. For whatever reason."

She ignored the blatant come-on, the smug self-satisfied tone of voice. The man's masculine ego knew no bounds. Still, he was carrying her bag for her, and she bit back a sharp retort.

"Actually," he went on as they walked along, "I'm leaving myself tomorrow."

Commander Perkins had mentioned that his work took him all over the world. "Oh? And where are you off to now?"

"Paris, first. Then possibly Japan."

They had reached her rental car by now. When she unlocked the trunk, he swung the suitcase up easily and set it down inside. Then he turned to her.

He was wearing dark glasses so she couldn't make out the look in his eyes—"the windows of the soul", as one poet put it—but the thin, rather sardonic smile on his lips made her uneasy.

"Thank you for your help," she said coolly. "Now, if you'll excuse me..."

She turned and started toward the driver's door, but he held out a hand, placing it lightly on her arm. She glanced down at the hand, then back up at his face, which once again was unreadable.

"Have a drink with me before you leave," he said.

She was about to give him a firm no when suddenly he reached up and removed the dark glasses. Although the green eyes gave away nothing, they were not hostile or mocking, merely friendly. One drink wouldn't hurt anything. If he was leaving tomorrow, she'd probably never see him again.

While she debated, she gave him a closer look. He was really a very attractive man once you got past that brusque, almost callous manner of his, and she could well understand what his red-haired friend had found so compelling.

The gold streaks in his dark hair glinted in the sunlight, his deeply-tanned face was well-molded, with high prominent cheekbones, a firm jaw, square chin, and softened by two deep indentations that appeared at the corners of his mouth when he smiled.

"Come on," he urged. "A well-disciplined lady like you must have allowed plenty of time to catch your plane."

It was on the tip of her tongue to blurt out the truth, that she had no plane to catch, but her innate caution and reserve held her back. It was none of his business that she'd decided to stay in Florida, had a job, was moving into an apartment.

She was hot and tired. A cool drink in the air-conditioned lounge sounded very tempting. Besides, something about the man intrigued her. He was so different from most of the men she'd known, men like Paul, her dead husband, all charm and impeccable manners on the outside, but shallow underneath.

This man had no charm whatsoever, but somehow she had the feeling that if any woman had the good fortune to penetrate behind the rough facade, she would find deep wells of character, even tenderness, that he kept well-hidden most of the time.

"All right," she said with a smile. "A drink sounds good."

Except for a few serious drinkers at the bar, they had the cool, dim lounge virtually to themselves at that hour. They sat down at a table and both ordered gin and tonic.

When their drinks arrived, he held up his glass. "Well, here's to you, Mrs. Trent," he said. "May you live long and prosper, as the saying goes, now that you've got your unfinished business taken care of."

She gave him a cool smile. "I think at this point, after all we've been through together, you might drop the Mrs. Trent. To tell you the truth, I'm getting a little tired of it."

He took a long swallow of his drink then smiled at her. "All right. Jessica. Or do they call you Jessie?"

"Never!" she said with feeling. "At least," she added, "not since school days. And I hated it then."

She took a healthy swallow of her own drink, then set the glass down carefully. "Speaking of names," she said, "I'm curious about yours."

"Luke?" he asked. "It's a common enough name. The apostle, you know."

"No, it's the Fury part I've been wondering about. I don't think I've ever heard it before."

He gave her a level look. "Perhaps not in your exalted circles, you mean, where everyone has more aristocratic names."

"Oh, stop it!" she said, frowning. "That kind of reverse snobbery is so stupid."

He opened his mouth, as though to deliver a sharp retort, but in the next instant his face softened, and he smiled. "You're right." He put his elbows on the small table and leaned toward her so that his face was only inches away from hers. "There's something about you, Jessica, that brings out the worst in me. You're so cool, so distant. Every time I see you I get this irresistible urge to ruffle your feathers."

The emerald eyes bored into hers so intently, flashing such fire, even in the darkened room, that there immediately popped into her mind a vision of just what he might *do* to ruffle her feathers, and she wasn't all that sure she would object.

Then she came to her senses and laughed. "Well, you do a pretty good job of it, I must say." She took another sip of her drink, more slowly this time. "But the name. Is it English?"

He shrugged. "Damned if I know. The nuns gave it to me at the orphanage. I was the proverbial baby left on their doorstep. Naturally they gave me an apostle's name, and the Fury came later. They said it suited my character. I was an angry little devil."

His tone was light, even flippant, but Jessica could sense the hurt behind it, and her heart went out to him. Instinct told her, however, that the one thing this man would never tolerate was sympathy.

"I can believe that," she said lightly, "since I know what it feels like to be on the receiving end of it."

"Yet you kept coming back for more," he said, suddenly serious. "I admire that. What I had to tell you must have been a blow, but you took it on the chin like a real soldier."

She shrugged. "I'd expected something like that. It wasn't really a surprise." She reached for her bag and rose from her chair. "Now, I really must go."

"But you haven't finished your drink."

"Yes, I have," she said. "As much as I want. Thank you again, Luke. For everything. And good luck on your new assignment."

CHAPTER THREE

JESSICA'S new apartment was tiny, just one room, really, with a foldaway bed, a kitchen alcove in one corner by the window and a small bath. In fact the whole thing would have fit nicely into her old bedroom at the Trent house, with room to spare.

Still, it was hers, and at least it was clean. It was also located in the center of town, on a bus line to the Naval base, and within close walking distance of shops, so that she was able to turn in her expensive rental car.

The furniture was shabby, but serviceable, and as she unpacked her belongings, she made a mental list of the things she'd need to set up house. There was still a sizable bank balance from Paul's insurance, so no need to panic over money, but the days of free and easy spending, knowing someone else would pay the bills, were over.

It was almost midnight by the time she finished getting her things put away, and she had a sudden urge to call Helen. The telephone seemed to be working, and since it was three hours earlier on the West Coast, she wouldn't be getting her out of bed.

Luckily it was Helen herself who answered. "Oh, Jessica," she said in obvious relief. "I've been so worried about you. When are you coming home?"

Jessica told her then about her plan to stay in Florida, her job at the base hospital, and as she did so, it occurred to her that it all sounded very unlike her, usually so docile, so willing to adapt to whatever was expected of her.

'Well!'' Helen exclaimed when she'd finished. ''I must say, that's a shocker. When did you decide all this?''

"Oh, I don't know. I just had an irresistible urge to try my wings in the world on my own.''

"Well, I must say you don't do things by halves, my girl. It doesn't sound like much of a job, though.''

"No, but if I work hard, who knows what it might lead to? The important thing is to take responsibility for myself for once.''

"Well, more power to you, Jessica.'' She paused for a moment. "Have you found out anything more about Paul's death?''

"Yes, finally. I'm afraid we were right. He had been drinking and he wasn't alone.''

"I see. Well, better to know the truth, I suppose.''

"Yes.'' She thought a moment. "Helen, was I a bad wife?''

"Heavens no!'' was the firm reply. "I loved that brother of mine, but he was without a doubt the world's worst husband. You stuck it out with him longer than most women would have.''

"I wonder if I shouldn't at least have gone to his funeral.''

"But my dear girl, you were flat on your back. You'd just lost your child. And Dr. Simpson would never have approved. Listen, Jessica, you've got to put all that behind you. After all, your marriage to Paul was over long before he died. The best thing you can do now is get on with your life. Meet

someone new. Marry again. Have the children you
wanted so badly.''

"Oh, there's no rush about that. Anyway, I'll
keep you posted about my progress. And thanks,
Helen, for everything.''

Several times during those first few weeks on the
job Jessica was ready to throw in the towel and call
it quits. She'd never thought of herself as a stupid
person, but she was so used to a more leisurely pace
that the pressures of the working world wore her
down.

Everyone was in such a hurry! The cafeteria pa-
trons were either so pressed for time they insisted
on immediate service, or they didn't have any cash
and wanted to sign a tab for their bill—strictly for-
bidden—or had to have certain denominations in
change, a seemingly endless stream of petty
problems, and all of them had to be solved *right
now*.

Each night she dragged home with aching feet,
shoulder muscles as tense as a board, and her head
full of figures. After three weeks she was certain
she'd either have to quit or get fired, and at that
point she didn't really care which.

She made mistakes in giving change. She was too
slow in her calculations. She totted up tabs wrong,
and even managed to lose one whole day's receipts.
Granted she found them later under the cash
drawer, but the whole experience unnerved her to
the point of panic.

Late one afternoon, during the usual pre-dinner
lull, she looked up from her register to see Millie
coming toward her, a grim look on her face, and

her heart sank. This was it! Poor Millie had finally had enough and was going to give her walking papers. She couldn't really blame her.

"Jessica," she said in her typical no-nonsense tone. "Would you mind changing your days and working weekends from now on? There's always such a rush then."

Jessica was so surprised—and relieved—that she could only gawk at Millie, open-mouthed. "You mean you want me to stay?"

"Of course I want you to stay. You're doing a great job."

"I am?" She laughed with sheer relief. "Well, you could have fooled me. I thought I'd managed to mess up at every turn."

Millie shrugged. "Oh, you've made your share of mistakes. We all do it in the beginning. But you catch on quick, and what's more, the customers like you. You have a nice way about you. That's very important in restaurant work. People can put up with wrong change far more easily than they can a sullen employee."

"Well, I'm glad to hear that," Jessica replied faintly. "But still a little surprised."

Millie gave her a wry smile. "As a matter of fact, so am I. To tell you the truth, kid, when you came waltzing in here that first day like the Queen of the May with your expensive clothes and your little note from the CO, I would have bet you wouldn't last two days—a week, tops."

Jessica sighed. "I'm afraid I do have that effect on people."

"Well, you do have a certain air about you, you know, society girl gone slumming, never done a day's work in your life. But I've got to hand it to you. You sure had me fooled. And I'm glad I was wrong. Keep up the good work."

High praise indeed, Jessica thought, from the hard-working and very efficient Millie, who was also a widow, with two small children to support. Then suddenly she heard a throat being cleared and saw that a customer was standing there waiting patiently.

"Oh, Dr. Palmerston," she said hastily. "I'm sorry. I must have been woolgathering."

"Never mind," he replied. "I'm not on emergency call today, so for a change I have plenty of time."

As she reached for his money and check his palm covered hers for a moment more than was necessary, and when she glanced up at him, there seemed to be a warm, even personal look in his light blue eyes.

She gave him a quick smile, made his change, thanked him, then watched him as he turned and walked away from her. She must have been mistaken. She hardly knew him, except as an occasional customer, but there was something oddly familiar about him.

Then, when he stopped at the entrance to speak to Millie it dawned on her. He was very much like Paul, the same blond hair and slim build, even the same smooth rather aristocratic air.

Suddenly he turned and came back to her. "Mrs. Trent," he said. Then, in a lower voice, "Jessica. I wonder if you'd care to have dinner with me one night next week. I have Wednesday and Thursday off, if you're free either night."

She hesitated a moment, debating. She had no friends in Pensacola, and now that she felt more secure about her job, perhaps it was about time she made some.

"Why, yes," she said. "I'd like that. Thursday would probably be better for me."

"Good. I'll pick you up. Around seven, shall we say?"

"That'll be fine," she said, and gave him her address.

When he was gone, Millie came strolling up to the desk, a broad grin on her face. "Well, my girl," she said. "It looks as though you've made a conquest of the hospital's prime catch."

"Oh, hardly that," Jessica replied, laughing. "One dinner doesn't count as a conquest. But how did you know?"

Millie chuckled. "Just a wild guess. Especially after he gave me the third degree about you."

"Third degree?" Jessica said stiffly.

"Don't get upset," Millie soothed. "He just wanted to know if you were married. A real gentleman, our Dr. Palmerston. Not into adultery, like so many of them around here. As I say, a prize catch. Comes from a wealthy family, too, I hear."

Jessica had the late shift that day, which ended at eight o'clock, after the dinner rush. The buses didn't run quite so often after six, so she'd either have to run two blocks to her stop to make the next one on time or wait another half hour.

As she hurried through the front door she saw a man walking up the steps toward her. It was already dark out, so it wasn't until he reached the light burning at the top of the stairs and raised his head that she realized who he was.

He looked up at her and for a moment they both stood stock still, staring and stared at. Then he came walking slowly toward her and stood directly in her path, a bemused smile on his face.

"Well, as I live and breathe," he drawled. "If it isn't Jessica Trent! What in blazes are you doing here?"

"Hello, Luke," she said. "Believe it or not, I work here."

"Working!" he exclaimed, after a brief double-take. "Will wonders never cease! What brought that on?"

"Oh, it's a long story. But what are *you* doing here? I thought you were off to Paris, Japan, and all points east and west."

He shrugged. "I finished up the Paris job sooner than I expected, and the Japan problem has been delayed. They needed me here to finish up some paperwork, so here I am."

"Well, I've got to run," she said, and started to move past him. "Or I'll miss my bus. In fact," she added, glancing down at her watch, "I probably already have."

"I'll drive you home," he rejoined immediately, and the next thing she knew he had taken her by the arm and was propelling her down the steps. "I'm on my way back to the motel myself."

Although Jessica didn't quite like the way he simply took over, obviously a habit of his, she was so grateful she wouldn't have to wait for the next bus that she followed along beside him.

"Actually," she said, when they were inside his car and he'd started the engine, "I don't live at the Paradise anymore. I have an apartment in Pensacola."

He turned to her with a puzzled frown. "Curiouser and curiouser," he commented briefly. "What brought that on?"

"Simple economics," she replied with a wry little smile.

He cocked an incredulous eyebrow at her. "You? Senator Trent's daughter-in-law?" He snorted loudly. "Don't make me laugh!" Then his eyes narrowed. "You're putting me on, aren't you?"

"Not at all. I needed a job. Commander Perkins helped me get one. And as it turns out, I'm pretty good at it." She laughed. "Much to everyone's amazement, I might add—including my own."

She had finally surprised him, she realized with a swift rush of satisfaction, actually left him speechless, and as they drove along in silence toward town, she watched him covertly.

He drove as he did everything else, competently, with brisk authority, taking no chances, but clearly in command. His hands rested lightly on the steering wheel, one elbow propped against the open window, the warm breeze ruffling his dark hair slightly.

He had a nice profile, in spite of the glowering forehead and firmly-set jaw. His nose was high-bridged, rather beaky, the cheekbones prominent, and she wondered about his parentage. He was heavily tanned, but the underlying olive cast to his complexion indicated Latin forebears, or perhaps, considering the nose and wide-set green eyes, a Slavic ancestry.

She became so engrossed in her study of the interesting face that she didn't realize she'd been staring at him until the car came to a sudden halt in front of her apartment, and she found herself gazing directly into his eyes.

"Well?" he asked in an amused tone. "Do I pass?"

Her glance faltered and she looked away in confusion. Then she raised her eyes again with a defiant lift of her head. Surely he must be as well aware of his compelling good looks as she was.

"I haven't decided," she said in a flat voice, and reached for the door handle. "Thank you very much for driving me home."

"Hey, wait a minute," he put in hastily. "Don't rush off like that. You still haven't explained what you're doing here."

She glanced back at him. "Yes, I have," she replied.

"Come on, now," he said, putting a hand on her arm. "Aren't you going to ask me up for a drink after I very nicely rescued you and gave you a ride home?"

"No, I'm not," she replied with a pleasant smile. "But thanks again for the lift."

"Well, then, how about having dinner with me?"

She hesitated. There was no denying the man intrigued her, even attracted her in a rather primitive way. But he also frightened her a little. She sensed danger in him, and at this point in her life, just getting on her feet, making her own way for the first time, she couldn't afford any complications.

She'd only be letting herself in for trouble if she ever let this man get close to her.

Finally she shook her head. "No. I don't think so."

He gave her a penetrating look. "You almost said yes, didn't you?" He raised a hand. "Never mind. I know I'd never get a straight answer out of you. But let's compromise. If you won't invite me in, and won't accept my very kind dinner invitation, at least come and have a drink with me."

"All right," she agreed reluctantly.

Surely, she told herself as she stepped out on the pavement, there could be no harm in one drink in neutral territory. She stood there waiting for him as he came around to join her, impressed once again by his pantherlike grace. He moved like a skilled athlete, well-controlled, but with instinctive ease.

"I know a little place just around the corner," he said, taking her lightly by the arm and walking on. "Not as elegant as what you're used to, but quiet and not too crowded."

"I wish you'd stop referring to what I'm used to," she said, annoyed. "Or what you think I'm used to. From the moment we first met you've been passing judgment on me, and you really don't know anything about me."

"Ah, but I'm anxious to learn," he rejoined instantly.

She had no answer to that, and they walked along in silence. He still kept a firm grip on her arm, and the sensations aroused by the feel of that rather rough hand on her bare skin were unsettling, yet oddly pleasant.

They soon came to a small unpretentious café, and he ushered her inside. The interior was quite dark, and it was very quiet, just the low murmur of largely masculine voices, and in the background the clink of glasses, the barely audible sound of soft music.

Luke's hands were on her shoulders now, guiding her toward a row of wooden booths at the back of the room. When he stopped at an empty booth his hands left her shoulders, and for a moment she felt a definite sense of loss.

"Sit down," he said. "I'll go to the bar to get our drinks." He grinned down at her. "That's the way it's done around here. What'll it be? Another Tom Collins?"

"Yes," she replied, impressed that he had remembered.

When he was gone she had to wonder what had possessed her to agree to come here with him. She didn't want any involvement at all, but especially not with a man like Luke Fury. What she should do is get up and walk out, now, before it was too late.

But by then it was too late. He was already on his way back, his large form blocking the aisle between the tables. He set the drinks down and slid into the seat across from her. "Here's to you, Jessica," he said, raising his glass and taking a long swallow.

"Thank you," she murmured, sipping at her own drink.

"Now," he said, setting his glass down and placing his elbows on top of the table. "Will you please tell me what's going on?"

"There really isn't anything to tell," she hedged.

"Come on, Jessica. I asked nicely." He leaned closer. "You intrigue me, lady," he went on in a low voice. "When I first met you I had you all pegged for a snob, the lady of the manor dealing with the scruffy hired help." She opened her mouth to protest, but he held up a hand, stopping her. "Then," he went on firmly, "I give you a piece of news about your husband that would have sent a lesser woman into hysterics, but you took it like a real trooper, and my respect for you went up several notches." He shrugged. "But that remote, touch-me-not air you have about you still put me off, and I figured you only spelled trouble for me." His eyes narrowed. "In spite of the fact that I was very attracted to you."

Jessica didn't know what to say. She'd suspected, of course, that he'd been coming on to her by his actions, the way he touched her, the innuendo in his voice, but figured it was all part of his act, nothing genuine about it. In her eyes, Luke Fury was a man who was well aware of his attraction for women and used it to make trophies out of them. Now she wasn't so sure.

"Well?" he said at last. "I've been open and honest with you about the way I feel. No tricks, no obfuscation."

She frowned down at her drink for a few moments, then looked up to find that glittering green gaze still boring into her. He looked so serious, even a little unsure of himself, as though he was out of his depth for a change, and didn't like it one bit.

Finally she gave him a tentative smile. "I'm not sure what it is you want from me, Luke," she said quietly.

"Well, for a start, you might tell me what the hell you're doing in Florida working at a menial job you surely don't need."

She had to laugh. "As a matter of fact, I *do* need the job. Aside from Paul's insurance, I have no money."

His eyes flew open, then narrowed in an expression of sheer disbelief. "Oh, please," he said with the hint of a sneer in his voice. "Give me a break. You've got to be putting me on."

"No," she assured him hastily. "I'm not. I'm telling you the pure unvarnished truth."

He leaned even closer, his face only inches away from hers now. "Do you mean to tell me," he began, his tone dead serious now, "that with all the Trent millions behind you, plus God knows how much more in your own family, you're reduced to working in the hospital cafeteria as a cashier just to pay the bills?"

She nodded, enjoying herself now. "That's right."

He slumped back in his chair and folded his arms across his chest. "Why?" he said at last.

She shrugged. "It's hard to explain. I just got tired of living off other people. Oh, don't imagine for a minute that I'm not well aware of what I've given up. It hasn't been any picnic for me to have to scrimp and save just to exist. But I have to tell you that I feel better about myself now than I have in a long time."

"Well, I'll be damned," he muttered softly. He shook his head. "You're an amazing woman, Jessica. There aren't many of you around with that kind of integrity."

She thought about Millie. "Oh, don't kid yourself," she said earnestly. "There are plenty of heroic women out there struggling to make it on their own, raising children by themselves, taking whatever job comes along." She took one last sip of her drink, then rose to her feet. "Now, I really must go."

He jumped up beside her. "I'll walk you home."

"Oh, no need for that."

"But I want to." He took her by the arm and started toward the front entrance. "Don't worry, I won't ask again to come in. You made it pretty plain you're not having any of that."

They were out on the pavement now, the street that was so crowded earlier now virtually empty. The soft evening air was balmy and redolent of the tang of salt water carried on the gentle breeze off the Gulf, and the tall palm trees that seemed to grow everywhere were swaying high above them.

When they came to her building, she turned to say good-night and thank him for the drink, but he was already moving forward, opening the door to the entrance.

"I'll just see you to your door," he announced.

"All right," she said, after a moment's hesitation. "I live on the second floor."

When they reached her apartment, she got out her key then turned back to him. "I'll say good-night now, Luke," she said with a smile. "And thank you for the drink. It was very pleasant."

Since the lights in the upstairs corridor hadn't yet been turned on, his face was cast in shadows, and she couldn't quite make out his expression. For a moment he neither spoke nor moved. Then, suddenly, one arm shot out and he put his hand flat against the wall behind her, virtually pinning her.

His other hand came to rest against her cheek, and he said in a low voice, "When can I see you again?"

She bit her lip and stared down at the floor, her feelings warring within her. She did want to see him again. In spite of his maddening self-assurance, she was very attracted to him. She found the few fleeting glimpses of a gentler side, a vulnerability that he kept well-hidden, even from himself, quite endearing.

But as strong as that attraction was, there was also something frightening about him. He himself made no bones about his life-style. He was a man on the prowl, a rolling stone that had no intention of tying himself to anyone or anything, going where he pleased, taking love where he found it, then leaving when it suited him. Could she afford to become involved with a man like that? Especially so soon after Paul's death?

She had just opened her mouth to turn him down, when one finger of the hand on her cheek came to press lightly against her lips. "Don't," he murmured softly. "Don't say no."

"I just don't think it would be a very good idea, Luke," she said in a low troubled voice.

"Why not?"

She looked up at him. "We're very different, you and I. You don't really approve of my background, and I can't even begin to understand yours. What could we possibly have in common?''

He gave her a slow smile. "I can think of one thing," he said, and before she could grasp his intention, his head had dipped down, and his mouth was brushing softly against hers.

It was as though a flame had suddenly been ignited within her. There was nothing remotely seductive or demanding about his kiss. His arm had come around her shoulders, drawing her gently up against the tall lean length of his hard body, but he wasn't clutching at her or pawing her, and in the next moment, he had raised his head and stepped back a pace from her.

"Well? How about it?" He grinned at her. "If you're worried about my making a pest of myself, I should tell you that I'll be leaving soon anyway."

"Oh, really?" she asked in a faltering voice, still stunned by the impact of that kiss. "Why is that?"

He shrugged. "The job here won't take long. I'm only waiting for the situation in Japan to get settled, then I'm off again."

"I see," she said carefully. "Then why bother?"

"Why not?" he rejoined instantly. "I like you. You intrigue me. I think we could have some good times together. And I'll most likely be wandering back this way eventually."

Still she hesitated, possibly even more reluctant now that he'd made it absolutely clear it was only "good times" he was after. She thought about Sandra, and wondered if she'd have to take a place in line behind her. And how many others?

She was just about to refuse him again, but he forestalled her. "Never mind," he said curtly. "I can see I'm wasting my time with you. You'll never get free of that high and mighty background of yours, and I'll always be the hired help. Forget it, lady. I don't need that kind of..."

"Oh, stop it!" she broke in angrily. "You know darned good and well it's not that."

"Do I?" he asked with a sneer. "Prove it."

"I don't have to prove anything to you," she retorted hotly.

Suddenly he smiled. "So," he said in a tone of intense satisfaction. "It *is* possible to get a rise out of you."

Still grinning, he gave her a mock salute, turned on his heel, and stalked off down the hall away from her. Just at that moment the hall lights went on, one of them striking him as he passed beneath it, catching the golden streaks in his dark hair.

She stood there staring after him until he disappeared from view down the stairs. He never once looked back.

In the days that followed, Jessica did her best to put thoughts of Luke Fury out of her mind. She'd been right to refuse him. He only meant trouble for her. She didn't need entanglements of any kind at this stage of her life, and especially not with that disturbing man.

By Thursday evening she also deeply regretted agreeing to have dinner with Greg Palmerston, the doctor from the base hospital.

"Men!" she said aloud to her bedroom mirror as she put the finishing touches on her makeup. It was almost seven o'clock, and she had a feeling Greg was the kind of man to show up on time.

At least he was safe, she thought as she brushed a stray wisp of dark hair back from her forehead. They came from the same kind of background. She understood what made him tick. Not like Luke Fury, who seemed hellbent on maneuvering her into a corner every time they met. She hadn't even seen him at the base since the night he'd driven her home, and that's the way she wanted to keep it.

She was just clipping on a pair of pearl earrings when the doorbell rang. She glanced at her watch. Seven o'clock on the dot! Somehow, she found that fact depressing. That kind of man was so predictable. One thing you could say for Luke, he made life a little more interesting, added a spark of zest to what was becoming a rather humdrum existence.

"Hello," she said, opening the door. "Right on time."

He grinned at her. "Oh, my mother always taught me that being late was one of the cardinal sins."

She nodded. "I know what you mean."

He flicked a quick glance over her. "I see you had the same kind of mother. You look as though you're all ready to go—and very lovely, too, in your blue dress. I like the color on you."

"Thank you, sir," she said prettily.

"Well, then, shall we go?"

His car was pretty much what she'd expected, a silver gray Mercedes, sleek and polished, just like Greg himself. Well-mannered man that he was, he held the door open for her and made sure she was seated before going around to his own side.

"I made reservations at the Paradise," he said as he pulled out into the traffic.

She gave him a quick sideways glance, not at all sure she liked that idea. There was too great a risk of running into Luke at the Paradise, since he seemed to stay there whenever he was in the area, and for a moment she didn't respond.

"I hope that's all right," Greg went on. "It's really the best place around to dine."

"That's fine," she replied with a quick smile. "I've eaten there before, and I agree with you."

As it turned out, the dining room was so crowded she wouldn't have noticed Luke even if he had been there. As usual, the food was delicious, the service excellent, and by the middle of her meal of fat juicy sweet and sour prawns, caught locally that day, she was feeling more relaxed than she had in months.

Greg was an attentive escort, and seemed genuinely interested in her as a person, quizzing her about her background, her family, her plans for the future. They even had several acquaintances in common, and it was good to catch up on the current news about them.

They had just finished dinner and ordered coffee when from across the room a woman's voice rang out. "Luke Fury! When did you get back? And why haven't you called me?"

Jessica's heart started to pound and she could feel her face going up in flame. Without thinking, she raised her head to scan the crowd. Eventually she spotted the red-haired Sandra, just rising from her stool at the bar and looking toward the entrance.

Then Jessica saw him. He was standing there, obviously just arrived, and she watched, transfixed, as Sandra ran over and threw her arms around him.

She suddenly realized that Greg had spoken to her. "I'm sorry, Greg," she said, turning back to him. "What did you say?"

But he had already swivelled his head toward the door. "Quite a display they're putting on," he remarked dryly. "Do you know him?"

"Only slightly," she said. "Do you?"

"Oh, yes," was the rather tart reply. "He has quite a reputation around the base. And I see he's living up to it tonight."

For some reason, Greg's rather sneering tone raised Jessica's hackles, but she covered it quickly. "She's very lovely," she said lightly. "Do you know her?"

"Not really," he replied with a shrug. "Not personally, that is. I do happen to know she's the daughter of an important general."

Jessica's eyes widened. "Oh, really? Not exactly a tramp, then, is she?"

Her sarcasm was lost on Greg, who only replied, "Hardly. I'll give Fury that much. He has pretty high standards when it comes to women. And," he added grudgingly, "from what I hear he's very good at his job." He reached across the table and put a hand over hers. "But enough about Luke Fury. I can think of several more interesting subjects to discuss with you."

Jessica smiled politely and gently withdrew her hand. Somehow the pleasant evening was spoiled for her, and her one thought now was to avoid having to speak to Luke.

From time to time, however, almost against her will, her eyes would dart toward the bar, where he and Sandra were still sitting, their heads close together, but he never once looked her way.

When Greg finished his coffee, he rose to his feet. "Excuse me for a moment, Jessica. I'll be right back."

As soon as he left, she turned to gaze out the window. It was quite dark out, with a crescent moon riding high in the night sky, the tall branches of the palm trees black against it. The surf shone with a phosphorescent glow as it broke on the gleaming white sand.

"Well," came a familiar voice. "Fancy meeting you here."

She turned her head to see Luke standing beside the table, his eyes hooded, a sardonic smile curling on his lips. Hiding her dismay, she managed to give him a thin smile.

"Hello, Luke," she said. "How are you?"

"Quite well, thank you. How are you?"

She frowned at the mocking tone in his voice. She should have known that simple good manners would be wasted on him. Now how was she going to get rid of him before Greg returned? She was about to put on her best lady of the manor air and ask him to leave, when Sandra appeared beside him.

"Oh, hello," she said with a smile. "It's Jessica, isn't it?"

Jessica nodded. "That's right. How are you, Sandra?"

"Oh, I couldn't be better." She turned to Luke. "We'd better leave if we're going to the Mitchells' party."

"Right," he replied briskly. He gave Jessica a curt nod. "Nice to have seen you again."

Sandra grasped him firmly by the arm and they turned and walked off together. Jessica knew she should be relieved, but as she watched him go, she couldn't help noticing that several other feminine glances were directed his way as he passed by, and she had to admit he was really a fine figure of a man, by far the most attractive one in the room.

Then why had she turned him down? It all seemed rather pointless now. She *was* attracted to him, and he to her. At least he had been. Now he'd found another playmate, and seemed to be quite reconciled to her refusal to see him again. And in spite of her best intentions, that fact rankled.

CHAPTER FOUR

IN THE NEXT few days, Jessica's feeling grew that she'd made a really stupid mistake in turning Luke away. It also stung that he obviously still considered her the worst kind of snob.

Now he wasn't even interested, and she couldn't really blame him. There was no use crying now over what was already done. Still, a light seemed to have gone out of her life. He had brought a little excitement into her rather drab existence, and she'd been a fool to be scared off so easily.

She kept looking for signs of him at the base, but every time she thought she recognized the dark head, the tall form with the broad shoulders and narrow hips, it turned out to be someone else.

When she finally did run into him, the following Saturday evening, it was under the worst possible conditions. She was just leaving the hospital after work when the black clouds that had been hovering overhead since noon suddenly burst into a heavy downpour.

She stood under the covered porch of the hospital gazing out with growing dismay at the steady torrent, hesitating. Hard to believe now, but the sun had been shining that morning. She simply had no choice. She'd have to go out in it, without an umbrella, or even a scarf. In fact, if she didn't hurry she'd miss her bus and have to stand out in the pelting rain for another half hour.

Finally, taking a deep breath, she plunged down the steps, covering her head with her handbag as well as she could, and started sprinting toward her stop. When she arrived, panting, she could just see, through the heavy curtain of rain, the taillights of her bus as it splashed its way down the street without her.

She stamped her foot in sheer frustration. Why had she stood there on the steps like a fool debating, as if she'd had a choice? For the first time, she regretted her decision to stay in Florida, the loss of the protected, pampered life she'd so blithely renounced just a month ago. She must have been out of her mind.

Just then, a car pulled up to the curb, the window came down and a voice called to her. "Want a lift?"

Although she recognized Luke immediately, at that point she would have gone with Jack the Ripper, just to get out of that blasted rain. She yanked the door open and slid inside.

"Oh, Luke, you're a lifesaver," she said with feeling. "But I'm afraid I'm going to drip all over your car."

"Not to worry," he replied, pulling away from the curb. "It's only a rental." He glanced over at her and chuckled deep in his throat. "My, if you aren't a sorry sight!"

She had to smile. "Oh, believe me, I'm well aware of that." Her hair was dripping, her dark blue suit sopping, her feet squishing in her sodden shoes. "If it's too horrible, just don't look."

He threw back his head and laughed out loud. "I've got to hand it to you, Jessica. You're a damned good sport, when it comes right down to it. Most women would have been fretting about their appearance and apologizing abjectly for it by now.''

She shrugged. "What's the point? I'm so glad to get out of that downpour, I couldn't care less what I look like.''

As they drove along, she did her best to mop up the worst of the rain on her arms, face and hair with her handkerchief, but it was a hopeless task. She'd be home soon, thanks to Luke, out of her soggy clothes and into a hot tub.

"So," he said, as he made the turn into her street. "How was your date with the good doctor?"

She gave him a swift sideways glance. "How did you know about that?"

"I was there. Remember?"

So he had kept track of her too that night, and must have seen Greg when he returned.

"Well?" he prompted. "How was it?"

"It was fine," she said shortly.

"Good. He's a nice guy. Good doctor, too, from what I hear." He grinned. "More in your class, too, I'm sure."

They had reached her building by now, and her heart began to thud in anticipation. Would he ask to see her again? If so, would she accept? Yes, she decided, and when he parked the car, the motor still running, she turned to him.

"Thanks so much for the ride, Luke," she said with a smile. "You saved my life. Another few minutes out there, and I think I would have drowned."

"My pleasure," he said.

She paused for a moment, hoping he'd go on. "Well, I guess I'd better go in," she said finally.

He nodded. "Better get out of those wet clothes, too."

Still she hesitated, waiting, hoping, but when he continued to sit there in silence, just giving her that same bland pleasant look, she knew he wasn't going to speak. Nor did she blame him. He wasn't the man to beg. Rejected once, he'd never come back for more. He'd only given her the ride out of pity, common human decency.

"Um, Luke," she said with a smile. "If you're not busy tonight, perhaps you'd let me repay you by cooking dinner for you."

Slowly his eyes flicked over her, his face a mask, not a trace on it of what he was feeling or thinking. While she sat there waiting for his response, her smile began to feel as though it were plastered on her face and she had to fight down a near-irresistible urge to fidget in her seat.

"No," he said at last. "I don't think so."

Although she was startled by his flat refusal, she rallied quickly and gave him another bright smile.

"Why not?" she asked lightly. "You did invite me out to dinner once, after all."

"And you turned me down," he said, a hard edge to his voice.

"Well, now won't you give me a chance to make it up to you and return the favor?"

He cocked one heavy dark eyebrow, gave her a thin smile and slowly shook his head. "Oh, I don't think I want to get involved with a woman like you," he drawled. "Too rich for my blood."

Her smile faded. "Listen, if you're going to start that nonsense about my lofty social background again..."

She stopped short when she heard him laughing, saw the tiny lines at the corners of his eyes crinkle in amusement. "I don't see what's so funny!" she stated angrily.

"God," he said, still chuckling deep in his throat, "I love to get a rise out of you." His eyes narrowed appreciatively. "You're really something when you get mad and let some of that inner fire show. It proves that there's a real woman under that cool exterior after all."

"Probably not your kind," she snapped.

"It also makes me wonder," he went on, ignoring the comment, his voice pitched in a lower more intimate tone. "What you'd be like in more pleasant circumstances."

She was about to retort hotly that there was no chance *he* would ever see her in those circumstances, when it suddenly dawned on her just how futile the whole conversation had become. She bit back the sharp comment, reached for the handle of the door and opened it.

"Good-night, Luke," she said stiffly. "Thanks again for the lift."

She jumped outside and made a dash through the pelting rain to the door of her building. It wasn't until she'd opened it and stepped into the blessedly dry foyer that she realized he had followed her inside and was now hard on her heels as she made for her own apartment.

She turned around and glared at him. "Are you still here?"

He gave her a hurt look. "Well, you *did* invite me to dinner."

"Yes, and you refused."

"Well, I've changed my mind. However, if you want to back out now..." he added with a lift of his broad shoulders.

When they reached her door she unlocked it and stepped inside. "Oh, all right, you might as well come on in," she said, and turned to see that he had followed close on her heels and was even now shutting the door behind him. "But then," she added wryly, "you already are, I see."

"So I am," he commented, flashing her a wicked grin.

She heaved an exasperated sigh. "Well, right now I'm going to get out of these wet clothes, then I'll see what I can find for dinner. Fix yourself a drink," she added, pointing to the low sideboard. "Make yourself at home."

Of course, he already had, and was now strolling around the tiny living room as though he owned the place, and it occurred to her as she headed toward the bedroom that Luke Fury was a man who would be quite at home in any surroundings.

As she showered and dressed she tried to keep her mind on what to give him for dinner, but she couldn't ignore the disturbing sensations his presence in her apartment had aroused, a slight buzzing in her head, a hollow feeling at the pit of her stomach, a more rapid pulse than normal, a longing she couldn't quite identify.

He was only a man, she told herself firmly as she dashed on a trace of pale lip gloss and smoothed down the skirt of her tailored cotton shirtwaister.

He'd done her a few favors, and now she was going to cook dinner for him. That was all there was to it. No need to react like a bedazzled schoolgirl.

When she returned, he was settled comfortably on the couch, drink in hand, the evening newspaper spread out on the table before him, and she stopped in the doorway, watching him. She hadn't realized how small the room was until now. He seemed to fill it with his presence.

Just then he raised his eyes to meet hers, and a slow smile spread across his tanned face. "All dry now?" he asked, rising to his feet.

"Yes." She started toward the kitchen. "I'll just see what I can find to eat." She gave a nervous laugh. "I'm afraid it won't be gourmet fare."

As she passed by, he reached out a hand and rested it lightly on her bare arm. "There's no hurry. Sit down and have a drink."

There was something about the look in his eye, lazy, slightly hooded, that worked on her already jangled nerves. What was there about this man that had the power to unsettle her so? Normally the most contained, unflappable of women, every time she was around him some inner wires in her head seemed to get crossed.

"Come on," he urged, tightening his hold. "Relax. I'll be leaving soon. We should get better acquainted before I go."

She darted him a swift look. "Leaving?" She felt both dismay and relief. "Well, then, there's not much point in getting better acquainted, is there?"

"Oh, I'll be back. Come on. Sit down and talk to me."

His hand slid slowly down her arm to grasp her by the hand, and reluctantly, she allowed him to lead her over to the couch. She sat down primly, the way she'd been taught, and folded her hands in her lap. He stood looking down at her, looming over her.

"Now, what'll you have to drink?"

"A glass of sherry will be fine," she said.

He nodded, and she sat there watching him as he poured it out. When he came back, glass in hand, he handed it to her, then sat down close beside her.

"Cheers," he said, raising his drink.

He was sitting so close to her that she could feel the warmth of his body through her thin cotton dress. She really should move farther away, yet he was sure to comment if she did. No point in making an issue of it.

"So," she said, setting down her glass. "You say you'll be leaving soon?"

He nodded. "Afraid so." He shifted his body around to face her, still touching her, and reached for her hand. "But I also said I'd be back, and I'd like to think you'll be here when I do."

She wasn't at all sure she liked the way the conversation was tending, not to mention his blithe possession of her hand, which he was now turning around in his, examining the place on her finger where her wedding ring had left a white mark.

"And what about your lovely redhead?" she asked lightly.

He raised his eyebrows. "Sandra?" He made a dismissive gesture with his hand. "She's only a friend."

She didn't believe that for a moment. Hadn't she seen them together with her own eyes? And the way they were acting certainly strained the limits of mere friendship. However, right now she had a more pressing problem to deal with.

His other arm had snaked around her waist by now. How he'd managed that without her realizing it escaped her, but it certainly implied long practice. She tried to edge away from him, but his hold only tightened.

"You know, Jessica," he said in a low voice close to her ear. "You intrigue me. You're not like any woman I've ever known." He put a hand on her cheek, turning her head so that she was gazing directly into those deep green eyes, glittering now with what she could only assume was desire. "And I think you feel it too, the attraction, the lure of the unknown."

She laughed nervously. "Isn't that a little dramatic? I'm really quite ordinary."

"Oh, no. Not ordinary at all," he replied. The hand was cupping her chin now, one long finger tracing the curve of her mouth.

In spite of all her good intentions, her conviction that this man was only playing with her, an insidious irresistible warmth began to steal through her. Something about those emerald eyes, the feel of his rough hand on her skin, the very scent of him, fresh and totally masculine, the hard body pressed so closely against her, made all her good resolutions evaporate.

The next thing she knew, the dark head had come down and his mouth was pressing against hers. Her head began to whirl. A tiny voice told her she should break it off now, before it got out of hand, but it felt so wonderful she couldn't make her body obey. Just the taste of him, a minty toothpaste, the Scotch he'd been drinking, went straight to her head, wiping out all her native caution.

His mouth was moving on hers now, drawing at her lips, and the hand under her chin moved downward to grasp the base of her throat. Suddenly, his mouth opened wider, and she could feel the pressure of his tongue, seeking entry. The only sound in the room was the heavy rasp of his breathing. Or was it hers?

Without thinking, her lips parted, and as his tongue darted inside, deepening the kiss, the hand on her throat slid farther down to settle on her breast. Even then, she couldn't move. The sensations he was stirring in her were too powerful to resist.

Dimly she realized that his fingers were now fumbling at the top button of her dress. She still couldn't move, but when the hand slid inside the loosened opening, and she felt his rough touch on her bare skin, she suddenly came to her senses.

She jerked her head up, breaking the kiss, and slid away from him, running a hand over her hair, redoing the button of her dress, looking away, unable to face him.

"What the hell?" he growled, reaching out for her again.

She eluded his grasp, jumped quickly to her feet and stood there glaring down at him. "No," she said.

His brow was like thunder. "No!" he exclaimed. "What do you mean, no?" He rose to his feet, put his hands on his hips, and glared right back at her. "You can't just disappear like that."

"Oh?" she said in her loftiest lady of the manor tone. "And whose rule is that?"

"Listen, lady," he said in a low menacing tone. "You invited me in here, remember? And you were with me all the way. Believe me, I can tell."

"I'm sure you can," she bit out. "Since you're so adept at these games."

For a few moments they stood there, eyes locked together in mortal combat. Then he gave an abrupt nod.

"So," he said in a sneering tone. "You were just stringing me along. Teasing me until you had me eating out of your hand, then freezing up when it suited you. There's a name for women like you, Jessica, and it's not very nice."

She crossed her arms in front of her and narrowed her eyes at him. "I made it clear to you from the day we met that I wasn't interested in your games," she retorted angrily. "What makes you think you have the right to make all the rules?"

He opened his mouth, then snapped it shut. "Not interested?" he ground out between clenched teeth. "You're lying, and you know damned well you are."

Suddenly it occurred to her how ridiculous the whole thing had become. They were both behaving like children. And he did have a point. While not exactly leading him on, she hadn't put up much resistance. The important thing now was to defuse the tense situation. After all, he was leaving soon. She'd probably never see him again. There was no point in parting enemies.

She forced out a smile. "Listen, Luke," she said in her most reasonable tone. "There's no reason for us to carry on this way. It was a misunderstanding. I'm sorry. It was probably my fault. You can be—how shall I put it—quite persuasive when you set your mind to it."

To her relief, the anger in his face gradually drained away. He stared down at his feet for a moment, rubbing a hand over the back of his neck, and when he looked up again he had even managed a quirky smile.

"You know, Jessica," he said. "If I didn't realize what a strong character you have, I'd say you were afraid of me."

"And with good reason, I'm sure."

He came a step closer, so that she could see each point of the faint dark stubble on his chin. "You have nothing to fear from me," he said softly. "Perhaps you're really afraid of yourself."

That suggestion came too near the truth for comfort, and she turned away. In spite of her determination to resist his practiced charm, there was still a part of her that yearned to prove to him that there was a real woman underneath the finely-honed exterior.

And he was right, she had nothing to fear from him. It was her own wayward impulses that terrified her. She'd never experienced anything remotely like the feelings he aroused in her, half-anger, half-desire.

"Of course," he was going on, "it could be you're only attracted to tame men. Like the good doctor, for example."

Stung, she turned back to him. "And you mean, like Paul?" She laughed dryly. "I'd hardly call that tame."

"Oh, Paul," he said with a shrug. "He was just weak."

"And you've cast yourself in the role of every woman's dream, I take it."

"Oh, not *every* woman," he replied with another diabolical grin. "I'm rather choosy. Of course," he went on, "I understand that my background might count against me with you. Even though I probably have the money you're used to, the fact remains that my origins were pretty questionable."

"Oh, stop it!" she cried, eyes blazing with rekindled anger. "I'm not interested in your money or your background. Can't you get that through your head?"

There, he'd done it again, got a rise out of her just when she'd thought she was in command of the situation. She also suspected he was laughing at her again, delighted at the success of his deliberate provocation.

"Under the circumstances," he said at last, "I think I'll pass on dinner." He started sauntering slowly toward the door, and when he reached it he turned around and gave her a long look, his lips still curled in that maddening smile. "And who knows, Jessica? Maybe our paths will cross again one day."

After he'd left, she made herself a toasted cheese sandwich and sat at the kitchen table picking at it, going over the unsettling scene with Luke again and again in her mind.

Had she behaved like an utter fool? If so, she couldn't quite decide whether it was by turning him away or by responding to him in the first place. Right now she certainly didn't need a man like Luke Fury in her life, not so soon after Paul's death.

Paul! With his good looks, impeccable background and perfect manners he was charming on the surface, but so weak underneath. Another man who considered anything in skirts fair game for his seductive charms. But there the similarity ended. Luke was brash and brusque, even callous, on the outside, but inside there was genuine substance, a rigid code of honor peculiarly his own.

As she sat there brooding and chewing glumly on her cheese sandwich, she felt a sudden urge to talk to her mother. It had been a long time since they'd spoken, not since Paul's death. A stiff, reserved woman whose life was dominated by the position she held as one of the leading lights of Boston society, they'd never been close.

Still, Jessica thought, setting down her half-eaten sandwich and getting up from her chair, there was something about one's mother that meant an understanding, a sympathy, that was irreplaceable.

It was still only eight o'clock. An hour or so difference in time zones wouldn't matter. She dialed the number, then stood there drumming her fingers on the counter impatiently, listening to it ringing, and when her mother's voice came on the line, tears came to her eyes.

"Hello, Mother," she said. "It's Jessica."

There was a short silence. "Well," came the distant reply. "This is a surprise. How are you, Jessica?"

"Oh, I'm fine. I just thought I'd let you know I'm staying on in Florida for a while."

"I see. Any particular reason? Or just for the sunshine?"

Jessica laughed nervously. "Well, as a matter of fact, Mother, I have a job."

Another longer silence. "A job?" her mother asked in a bewildered tone. "What kind of job?"

Jessica's heart sank. It had been a mistake to call. She'd been foolish to expect any kind of understanding of what she was trying to do with her life from her strait-laced mother, who still believed that a woman was only an adjunct of her husband's life, a social asset, a hostess, a mother to his children, but not much else.

"Well," she replied faintly, "I'm afraid it's not much, but it does make me feel good to earn money on my own."

"But you don't need money, Jessica," her mother said with elaborate patience. "I'm sure Paul's family are happy to take care of your needs, and you know you're always welcome to come back to Boston and live at home again. In fact, I could use an extra pair of hands with this exhibit I'm organizing for the museum."

She went on then into a long explanation of the trials and tribulations of finding adequate assistants, the recalcitrance of artists who refused to donate their services to such a worthy cause, the inevitable flare-ups of temper that only she could deal with.

Jessica stood there in a daze, listening to all the old familiar complaints and problems, the internecine warfare that always seemed to be a part of her mother's good works, and she knew, beyond the shadow of a doubt, that she could never go back to that kind of life again. Finally there was a lull in the seemingly endless stream of words, and she seized her opportunity.

"Well, Mother," she put in hastily, "I'm sure you'll do your usual wonderful job and it will all turn out right in the end. Thank you for inviting me, but I think I'll stay here for a while yet. The sunshine, you know," she added wryly.

"Well, of course you must suit yourself, Jessica, and if it amuses you to play at this job of yours, I certainly won't interfere. You really should consider Senator Trent's position, however. If word got out that his daughter-in-law was working at a menial job, it might reflect on his reputation."

"Oh, I'll be very careful," Jessica replied wearily. "I won't inform the newspapers." She took a deep breath and went on quickly before her mother got a chance to reply. "Well, it was nice talking to you, Mother. I'll call again soon. Good-bye for now."

Carefully, quietly, she hung up the receiver.

That conversation with her mother had made her more determined than ever to stick to her job, her new independent life, her very own apartment. Although she had bouts of loneliness, the sense of self-respect she'd gained made it worth it.

She didn't see Luke again. He'd obviously gone on to his new job, and although she missed him, she knew it was just as well. There was no future for her there.

* * *

One evening a few weeks later, Greg Palmerston came into the cafeteria just as she was totaling up the day's receipts and made straight for her counter.

"Hello, Jessica," he said. "Got time for a cup of coffee?"

"Why, yes," she replied with a smile. "Just let me put this away and lock the cash drawer first."

Just then they were interrupted by a voice booming from the intercom above the door. "Dr. Palmerston. Paging Dr. Palmerston."

Greg made a face. "Sorry, Jessica. Duty calls."

"Of course," she replied. "I understand."

"What I really wanted was to ask you to have dinner with me again this Saturday. There's a new Thai restaurant in Panama City that I hear is quite good. How about it?"

"Why, yes," she replied. "I'd like that."

When he was gone, Jessica went into the kitchen for a last cup of coffee. Millie was there, just winding up her nightly inspection. She flashed Jessica a meaningful grin.

"So," she said archly. "I see you've made quite a hit with the good doctor. Congratulations. Every waitress here has tried, but it's obvious you're more his style."

"And what does that mean?" Jessica asked lightly, pouring out coffee from the large metal urn.

Millie shrugged. "Oh, you know. Same background, same well-bred air. You could call it class."

Jessica whirled around. "Why, Millie, I'm surprised at you. I hope I've never done or said anything to make you think..."

Millie held up a hand. "Oh, it's nothing you've done. It just sticks out a mile, all over you. The way you walk, your tone of voice, the way you dress. Listen, I'm not passing judgment, and I don't mean to sound critical. If you've got it, flaunt it, is what I always say. Anyway, you two obviously belong together. I'm happy for you. And for him. He's a nice guy."

"Yes. I think so too."

"In fact," Millie went on, a little hesitantly this time, "I'd much rather see you get involved with him than with Luke Fury." She shook her head. "That man only spells trouble."

Jessica frowned. "Now, what makes you bring him up? There's no connection between us."

"Oh?" Millie raised a disbelieving eyebrow. "Listen, kiddo, I've seen the two of you together, and I've known Luke a long time. He gets a certain look in his eye when he's on the prowl. Believe me, you'd be a real challenge to him, and to men like Luke, a challenge is like a nice chunk of steak to a hungry dog."

"Well, you don't need to worry about that," Jessica replied firmly. "There never has been anything between Luke Fury and me and there never will be. You can count on that."

Millie started toward the door. "I'm glad to hear it," she called over her shoulder. Then she stopped and turned around. "Just don't protest too much, Jessica," she added in a softer tone.

When she was gone, Jessica stood there, her untouched coffee cooling in her hands. What had brought that on? What had made Millie think there even *might* be something going on between her and Luke? Of course, she added to herself, reddening slightly, she hadn't told Millie the whole truth. But that was in the past, a closed book. No need to say anything about it.

Her dinner date with Greg went off pretty much as she'd expected. He was such a predictable man that she could relax around him. In that respect, Millie was right. He was so much like the men she'd known all her life, with his familiar little courtesies and conversation.

But wasn't that exactly what she'd stayed in Florida to get away from? Paul had been just such a nice well-bred man on the surface, knew all the right things to do, at ease in every social situation. So was her father-in-law, Senator Trent. And yet it was Paul who had deceived her, the senator who had moved heaven and earth to cover up the truth about his son's death.

Luke Fury, on the other hand, was the most unpredictable person she'd ever met. Gruff and curt one moment, passionate and caring the next. She'd seen his softer side, the deep reserves of tenderness and vulnerability he tried so hard to hide.

However, they were worlds apart in everything that mattered. He seemed to think of love as a game, played for temporary amusement, then abandoned when it was won, while to her it was deeply serious. Then why, she asked herself bitterly, did she find it impossible to get him off her mind?

It was June now, and growing warmer each day, even on the balmy Gulf Coast. On her next day off, Jessica followed her usual routine. She spent most of the morning cleaning the apartment, then after a late lunch, showered and got ready to go out and take a short walk on the nearby public beach before doing her week's grocery shopping. She always dressed carefully whenever she went out in public, a habit firmly-instilled in her from early childhood.

She'd recently bought two inexpensive cotton sundresses to wear when she went out on her errands. Today she chose the white one, a simple shift, loose-fitting, the low neckline cut square across and held up by two thin straps, and set off her deepening tan nicely. She slipped her feet into a pair of low-heeled sandals, gathered up her straw handbag and went out into the street.

The bright sunlight was dazzling, and she stood there for a moment, squinting. Then, just as she reached into her bag for her sunglasses she noticed the car parked directly in front of her building, the tall dark-haired man leaning back against it, his arms folded across his chest.

It couldn't be, she thought, staring, but as he pushed himself away from the car and started walking slowly toward her, she knew it was Luke. He looked marvelous, dressed in a pair of black chinos that set off his long legs and narrow hips, and a white knit shirt that revealed strong tanned arms. The gold streaks in his dark hair glinted in the sunlight.

He was smiling broadly at her, one hand raised in greeting. "How about a lift?" he said, coming to stand before her.

She slipped her dark glasses on and looked up at him. "Hello, Luke," she said quietly. "When did you get back?"

"Just last night."

"Then I take it the job in Japan is finished."

He nodded. "For now."

She couldn't help smiling. "And how long have you been out here lying in wait for me?" she asked.

He glanced at his watch. "Oh, about half an hour. Well? How about it? Where are you off to?"

"I was just on my way to the beach," she explained. "It's cooler there. Then there's grocery shopping."

He stopped and put a hand lightly on her arm. "Fine," he said, falling into step beside her. "We'll go for that walk first, then I'll help you with your shopping."

She gazed up at him, hesitant, frowning. Once again he'd simply taken charge. He too was wearing dark glasses, so that she couldn't quite make out the expression on his face.

"Come on, Jessica," he said in a low coaxing voice. "I won't bite. Besides, there are a few things we need to discuss." He gave her a rather grim smile. "If you recall, we didn't part on the best of terms, and it's been on my mind."

They were standing in the middle of the busy sidewalk, obstructing the pedestrian traffic, people jostling past them, a few with rather angry mutterings about owning the sidewalk. She had to make up her mind quickly. Somehow, the prospect of a solitary walk didn't appeal nearly as much as it had before he showed up.

"All right," she said at last.

"Good." He grasped her more firmly by the arm and they set off together toward the beach.

CHAPTER FIVE

THE PUBLIC beach was quite crowded, mostly with families. There seemed to be hordes of children, playing ball, splashing in the surf, building sand castles, chasing each other and screaming. Jessica and Luke stood at the end of the path for a moment watching, and when she gave him a questioning look, his face creased in a heavy frown.

"Let's try a little farther up," he said, taking her firmly by the arm. "Away from those dratted kids."

"Don't you like children?" she asked as they started walking away from the crowd.

"Only in small doses," was the flat reply.

"But surely you must want your own some day."

He gave her a startled look, then snorted loudly. "Who me? Some father I'd make! To be a good father, one needs to have had some experience of paternal love."

"Not necessarily. It's even possible a fatherless man could be an even better parent to his own children. You know, make up for what he'd missed."

"That's just pop psychology, and coming from a woman who's had all the advantages of an ideal childhood, I'm afraid it doesn't cut much ice with me." Although he was smiling down at her, there was a hard edge to his voice.

"That's not quite fair," she protested. "You know nothing about my childhood. There are lots of ways of being disadvantaged. I grew up in a straitjacket, suffocated by tradition and what was expected of me. It only made me even more anxious not to raise my own children that way."

He didn't say anything for a while, but when he spoke again she knew she hadn't made a dent in his thinking. "You could be right, I suppose," he said at last. "But even if I were slated to become the best parent in the world, my job takes me away so much of the time I wouldn't be much use to children, not to mention its more dangerous aspects."

He had a look on his face that she'd learned meant the subject was closed, and they continued to walk slowly along the water's edge in silence, the fine white sand crunching under their feet until they finally reached an area where the beach was less crowded, with only a few children and their parents splashing in the clear, blue-green water. The tide was coming in, and as the gentle surf encroached, they gradually moved over to the narrow path beneath the long row of tall palm trees.

They stopped at a high chain link fence that separated the public beach from its neighbor, and Luke stopped, pointed to the low outcropping of rock beside it under the shade of a giant gnarled live oak tree.

"Shall we sit down for a while?" he asked.

"Yes. I could stand a breather."

She turned to survey the distance they had come, raising a hand to her forehead for protection against the dazzling sun, now, in late afternoon, still high in the sky. When she turned back to him, he had removed his dark glasses and was staring at her intently, his expression grave. As their eyes met, something seemed to catch in her throat, and for a moment she faltered under that steady scrutiny.

Then she said lightly, "I can see now why I'm so tired. We've come quite a long way."

She started past him toward the rocks, half-expecting him to reach out for her, and her heart began to beat a little faster. Whatever it was she was feeling, he clearly felt it too. That look they'd exchanged had been full of meaning. But he only fell into step beside her, and they sat down next to each other, not touching.

There was something hypnotizing about the steady pounding beat of the surf, wave upon wave rolling in over the sparkling sand, then receding to start the process all over again. Although they didn't speak, the still, humid air seemed to crackle between them.

To break the tension, she turned to him and broached a neutral subject. "Tell me about Japan."

"All right. What do you want to know?"

She laughed. "Everything. I've never been there, but I hear it's a delightful place, and very beautiful."

"Yes, it is, although I didn't have much spare time to enjoy the sights. I was kept pretty busy on the job."

"And what was that?"

He gave her a dubious look. "Are you sure you're interested? Most women find my job either boring or gruesome." He gave her that heart-stopping look again. "But then, you're not most women, are you, Jessica?"

That intense green gaze was setting up a familiar disturbance, and she looked away. "Oh, I'm really quite ordinary," she said with a laugh. "And in any case, I really do want to hear about it."

"Well, let's see. There had been a collision between two light planes at a small airport just outside Tokyo, and they called me in to investigate, try to discover the cause."

"And did you?"

"I think so. At least the Japanese officials were satisfied. They actually had it pretty well figured out themselves, and only needed me for corroboration of their own findings."

"You like your work, don't you?"

"Oh, yes. Very much. Not only the job itself, but the fact that it takes me to such interesting parts of the world."

"Yet you said yourself it's dangerous."

He shrugged. "Yes, it can be, especially if I have to test a damaged plane, but I don't dwell on that aspect of it."

No, she thought, smiling to herself, I'll bet you don't. In fact, if she knew anything about Luke Fury, the danger was probably the most attractive aspect of his job.

"Well," she said aloud. "You're obviously very good at it."

He gave a short dry laugh. "Whatever success I've had is certainly a far cry from what everyone expected would become of me. I don't think the poor nuns at St. Bridget's Children's Home have recovered to this day from what I put them through as a kid."

"It couldn't have been that bad," she chided. "Surely you must have had some redeeming qualities."

He flashed her a grin. "Nope," he replied. "Not a one." Then his face darkened. "I was so damned *angry* all the time," he said almost under his breath. "It just seemed as though no one . . ." He waved a dismissive hand in the air. "But that's all water under the bridge." He inched closer to her, their bodies just barely touching now. "I'd much rather talk about you."

"Now that *is* the most boring subject in the world," she said with a laugh.

She deliberately made her tone lighthearted, but even as she spoke she was searching his face, wondering what it was he'd been about to say. It just seemed as though no one—what?

It could only be one thing. As an abandoned child, surely he must have believed no one had loved him. Then typically, the moment he touched on the pain of his childhood, he veered away from it, covered it over with the hard shell that had become second nature to him and quickly changed the subject.

She felt a sudden yearning to get behind that protective veneer, to penetrate the facade. Just the fleeting glimpses into his inner feelings he'd allowed her so far told her that what he was covering up was exactly what endeared him to her, that vulnerability, that woundedness, and made him lovable.

"Well," he was saying now. "How about your marriage? Do you feel like telling me about that?"

"Oh, that's the most boring part of all. In fact, I've been thinking lately that I only came alive after Paul died. Is that a terrible thing to say?"

"Not if it's the truth. I take it you weren't exactly madly in love with him, then."

"Oh, I thought I was, of course, or I wouldn't have married him. It just seemed so right. Both families were for it, claimed we were perfectly suited." She laughed dryly. "What they really meant was that our marriage suited *them*, or their ideas of what was best for both of us." She turned to him and gave him a direct look. "And you of all people must know that he didn't really love me."

"Well, if not," was the gruff reply, "then he was a damned fool."

This time he did reach out for her. When she felt his arms come around her, she closed her eyes and allowed herself to sink up against him. For several moments they neither moved nor spoke, then, gently, he put a hand under her chin, lifting her face up to his.

"I don't know what it is about you, Jessica," he said in a low hoarse voice. "You seem to bring out the best in me." He smiled a little sadly. "And the worst, to be honest. For example, right now what I'd really like to do is rip that fetching little white dress off your back, throw you down on the sand and ravish you."

"Luke!" she cried, drawing back from him.

"Only kidding," he said, reaching out for her again. "No," he amended when she had settled against him again. "I wasn't kidding, but I've got sense enough by now not to try it. And I certainly didn't mean to be insulting."

She'd been shocked by his bald statement of desire, but insulted? Not in the least! In fact, it had set up some rather X-rated visions in her own head, and before they became too inviting, she drew away from him again, this time not quite so abruptly.

"It's getting late," she said softly. "And it's a long walk back. Perhaps we'd better go."

He frowned, and she primed herself for another battle of wills. But then he gave her a grim smile and rose slowly to his feet. "All right. You're the boss."

They walked back slowly in silence, each wrapped in his own thoughts. She'd been the one to stop whatever had been about to happen, and now she was beginning to regret it. Just walking along beside the tall man, so intensely aware of his sheer physical presence, was enough to set her pulses racing and weaken her knees.

When they arrived back in town, he stopped short and looked down at her. "Do you really have to go?"

"Well, I should, if I'm going to get my chores done."

"Can't you do your chores another time? We could both use a drink after our walk. Then maybe have some dinner."

"Well, I don't know about dinner. I'm a working girl now, remember, and have to take advantage of my days off."

His face closed down, the smile faded and somehow she was certain that if she turned him down again it would be the last chance she'd get. In fact, if she knew anything about him at all, he'd already stretched his capacity for tolerance to breaking point by coming back to seek her out today.

She smiled. "But I would like a drink."

"All right," he said grudgingly. "If that's the best you can do, I guess I'll have to settle for it." He looked around, then took her by the arm and started walking toward a small restaurant across the street.

They went into the cool dark lounge and sat down at a table by the window overlooking the shore. It was almost five o'clock by now, but the summer sun was still bright in the blue sky, hanging in the western sky like an enormous lantern and casting a golden swath over the sparkling water.

While Luke went up to the bar to get their drinks, Jessica watched him covertly, the tall carriage, the easy elegance of his long stride. If only he weren't so damnably attractive! She was already regretting her refusal of his dinner invitation. Still, it really was more sensible to move cautiously where this impetuous man was concerned.

Of course she was very attracted to him. Who wouldn't be? And that short intimate moment on the beach had gone straight to her head. But she still sensed danger in him, really knew nothing about him, except for the terse snippets of information she'd almost had to pull out of him. What made a man like Luke tick? He was so different from any other man she'd ever known that she could already be getting in way over her head.

He came back shortly, a tall frosted glass in each hand, and they sat there for a few moments sipping their drinks, not saying anything. His head was turned away from her, gazing out at the gulf, his face in repose, the strong features relaxed, and she noticed for the first time the tiny lines at the corners of his eyes, the deeper indentations running from his fine straight nose down to his mouth.

"How old are you, Luke?" she asked on a sudden impulse. "Do you mind my asking?"

"Of course not. I'll be thirty-eight in November. Just ten years older than you."

Her eyes widened. "How did you know that?"

He smiled. "Oh, I make it my business to thoroughly research everyone with close connections to pilots who crash. Nothing personal," he added hastily. "It's just part of the job."

"I see." She thought a minute. "If your birthday is in November, you must be a Scorpio."

He nodded. "Afraid so."

She laughed. "I don't know anything about astrology, but I do remember hearing once that the typical Scorpio could either be a huge success in life—or end up in prison." She gave him a mischievous look. "Also that you might hate them or love them, but the one thing you could never do was ignore them."

He threw back his head and laughed. "Well," he said, "maybe I'm the exception that proves the rule."

Somehow she doubted that, but she had the feeling she'd already said too much on the subject. "So, tell me. Where are you off to next?"

He shrugged. "I never really know. The jobs come along, then I pick and choose which ones sound interesting, and I'm off."

"Well, what's your favorite place, then?"

He didn't even hesitate. "Oh, Japan. In fact, I may even live there permanently one day, when I retire."

She had to laugh at that. "Oh, you'll never retire!"

He quirked a dark eyebrow at her. "No? Why do you say that?"

She didn't feel she could tell him her real reason, that he was too full of energy and self-confidence, and obviously too good at his job, which was a unique one, to ever consider giving it up unless he became physically unable to perform his duties. And she couldn't imagine that ever happening.

"I don't know," she said instead. "I just haven't met very many people who seem to love their work the way you do. But don't you get tired of living out of a suitcase? Not having a real home?"

"I've never had a real home," he remarked with another lift of his broad shoulders. "Since I do spend a lot of time at the Naval Air Station here in Pensacola, I guess the Paradise is as close to a home as I'm likely to get."

His tone was offhand, but she found his words very sad. Although her own home life had been repressive, and she had no desire to return to it, she couldn't imagine not having some kind of place to call one's own, even her tiny apartment.

"Well," she said brightly, "I do envy you all the exotic places you've visited. I've done very little traveling."

He took a long swallow of his drink, draining it, then set the glass down on the table and leaned toward her. "Well, perhaps we can remedy that," he said softly.

She dropped her eyes, not quite sure how to take that. Was he suggesting she might go with him on one of his trips? Or merely that her day to travel would come some time in the future? Whatever it was, the prudent thing was to ignore it.

"Perhaps," she murmured. She finished her own drink, then pushed her chair back. "Right now, I think I'd better travel back to town if I'm going to get my chores done before dark."

For a moment it looked as though he was going to argue with her, but then he only nodded and rose to his feet. "All right," he said. "Let's go."

He insisted on helping her shop, then on walking her to her door, carrying her groceries and setting them down inside the apartment.

"Well?" he asked when she turned to him.

"Thank you for the help, Luke," she said, slightly puzzled at the questioning note in his voice. "And the walk and the drink. It was a pleasant afternoon."

He moved a little closer to her. "Aren't you going to ask me in?"

"I don't think so," she replied carefully. "As I told you, I still have things to do."

He shrugged and grinned down at her. "So you did. But you can't blame a man for trying. When can I see you again?"

She looked away, thinking. Would it be wise to encourage any kind of relationship with such a man? Here today, gone tomorrow, God knew where. What would be the point? But even beyond that, the danger she sensed in him made her uneasy.

"How about dinner tomorrow night?" he persisted.

"All right," she agreed at last. "But I don't get off work until eight."

"Then we'll make it a late one. Shall I pick you up here or at the hospital?"

"Better make it here."

He nodded and gave her a knowing look. "Ah, yes. Don't want tongues to wag, do we?"

"No," she said firmly. "We don't."

A slow grin spread across his face. "I love it when you get on your high horse," he said, and before she could think of the proper dignified response, his head had come down, his hands were on her shoulders, and his mouth was pressed against hers.

He held the kiss for a long time, with a gentle pressure at first that gradually became more demanding. Then, just as she was about to break it off, he raised his head and gazed down at her, his hands still holding her, slightly rough on her bare arms.

"Until tomorrow, then," he said in a low voice.

For the next few weeks Jessica's life seemed to be full of Luke Fury. The very next day a box of beautiful long-stemmed red roses was delivered to her door just as she was setting out for the hospital, and from then on flowers arrived so often that she had to buy new vases to put them in.

She saw him almost every night. If they hadn't made a specific date, he'd be waiting for her in front of her apartment when she got home from work. Sometimes he took her out to dinner, and on a few occasions she cooked for him. By tacit consent, they never met on the base, not difficult to do since their paths rarely crossed.

Gradually, her fears about his intentions were allayed. Although he kept trying to get past her defenses, she had managed so far to keep him at a safe distance, allowing him only a chaste good-night kiss, and that more as a friend than a lover.

What amazed her was that he kept coming back for more. She'd been certain that a man as successful with women as he appeared to be would simply write her off at the first sign of resistance. He never actually gave up trying, but whenever she stopped his roving hands or pulled away from a kiss that threatened to get out of hand, he seemed to take it philosophically, and never complained.

The only problem was that it grew harder and harder to resist him. There was no question about his own desire. He made no bones about it. He wanted her, and he'd keep trying until she gave in. He wouldn't insist, wouldn't force himself on her, but she sensed the absolute certainty in him that in the end he'd get what he wanted.

And that was fast becoming what she wanted, too. Then why was she holding him at bay? Several reasons, actually. Her bad marriage had made her wary of all men. The scars from Paul's infidelities still hadn't healed. And she was a recent widow, after all.

But as she searched her heart, she knew that at bottom the true reason was that she was waiting for some indication that Luke cared something more about her than a bed partner, another easy conquest. Just one small sign of love and she'd probably follow wherever he wanted to take her.

* * *

Unless it was on the evening before her regular days off, she made a point of turning him out early. Now that she'd had a taste of independence, her job meant too much to her to jeopardize it by showing up late or too tired to function effectively. He always took this in good part, too, and never argued with her when she told him she had to say good-night sooner than he would have liked.

On one of those early nights, he had just left, and she was on her way to bed, when the telephone rang. Frowning, she glanced at her watch. It was almost eleven o'clock.

It turned out to be Helen, calling from San Francisco.

"Helen, do you know what time it is?" she said with a laugh.

"Yes, eight o'clock," was the reply.

"You've forgotten the time difference again. It's easy to do, I know. It's three hours later here."

"I'm sorry. Did I get you out of bed?"

"No. In fact I just got home a few minutes ago."

"Oh? Heavy date?" Her tone was light, but the very real curiosity underlying it was obvious.

Jessica hesitated a moment before replying. Then suddenly she had an overpowering urge to talk to someone about Luke. Since they hadn't advertised their relationship around the hospital, and Helen was thousands of miles away, safely on the Pacific Coast, she was the perfect confidante.

"Well," she began slowly, "to tell you the truth, I have met a man."

There was a short silence. "I see," Helen said at last. "What's he like?"

Jessica laughed. "He's so different from any other man I've ever known that it's almost impossible to describe him. I still have trouble reading him myself."

"How, different?"

Jessica thought a minute. "Well, rougher around the edges, for one thing."

"Sounds fascinating!" was the dry response. "Tell me more. You make him sound like some kind of thug. He doesn't beat you, does he?"

"No," she replied with a laugh. "Far from it. What I mean is that he doesn't have the slick veneer or social polish of most of the men I'm used to. Yet, oddly enough, that very fact is a large part of his charm."

"Do go on," Helen prompted eagerly.

"Well, it's hard to explain. He might be rough, even abrasive at times, but there's an honesty about him I find very attractive. He is what he is, no pretense, no fake sophistication." An image of Luke leapt into her mind, and she had to laugh. "He also has a self-confidence that borders on arrogance. It's as though he's saying to the world in general, 'Take me or leave me as I am. I don't care.'"

What she couldn't tell Helen was what an intensely physical man he was, with an aura of near-palpable sexual electricity about him that awakened depths of response in her she'd hardly known existed. And that for the first time in her life she felt like a desirable woman instead of a mere social asset.

"And what does this paragon look like? Tall and dark and sexy?"

"Well, that just about covers it," Jessica replied.

"You don't mean it!" Helen clucked her tongue. "Well, hang onto him, dear. Is it serious?"

"Oh, I doubt it. Luke doesn't think the way we're used to. He has a job that takes him all over the world, footloose and fancy free, and I don't believe he'll ever settle down. Doesn't even want to. He likes his life just the way it is, and there's no place in it for a permanent commitment of any kind."

"Well, watch it, Jessica," Helen said in a warning tone. "That kind of flame can singe the wings of trusting little moths like you."

"Believe me, I'm well aware of the dangers, and I have no intention of getting burned. Forewarned is forearmed, you know. There's not much chance of this moth trusting in what Luke has no intention of delivering."

"Just be careful. These things have a way of sneaking up on you, no matter how forearmed you are."

"I agree, especially since it's so soon after Paul's death. Even though nothing has really happened between us, I can't help feeling that such a recent widow shouldn't even be seen in public with another man."

"Oh, bosh!" Helen exclaimed. "You know how I feel about that old nonsense. Paul ran you such a hellish life while he was alive, I see no reason for you to go into a year's mourning for him, or whatever the current rule might be. You deserve a little happiness, Jessica." She cleared her throat loudly. "So, other than lover-boy, how are things?"

Jessica filled her in on the job, the apartment, life in Florida, then they said good-night.

*   *   *

The next day Greg Palmerston stopped by the cash-ier's desk to ask her to have dinner with him that night.

"Oh, I'm sorry, Greg," she said. "I already have a date."

"I see. You know, I've tried to call you several times at home, but you always seem to be out." He paused a moment, then went on in a casual tone. "Shall I back off, Jessica? I mean, there's not much point in my trailing after you if you're involved with someone else, is there?"

For some reason his tone rankled. He seemed to be saying that unless he were the only man in her life, she wasn't worth wasting his time over. That was so typical of Greg's whole breed. They never even thought to consider how they really felt about anything, only how it would look.

She gave him a cool smile. "You'll have to decide that yourself, Greg. All I can say is that I happen to be busy tonight."

"All right," he said, frowning. "That's clear enough."

He turned and stalked away from her, passing by Millie on the way without so much as a nod. Millie continued on toward the desk, a quizzical look on her face.

"What bit him?" she asked. "He's usually so friendly."

Jessica laughed shortly. "I'm not sure, but I think I might have put a slight dent in his ego."

"Ah," Millie said with a knowing grin. "Like that, is it? Funny, I thought he'd be just your type."

"Maybe that's the trouble."

Millie continued to stare at her, as though waiting for more, putting Jessica in somewhat of a quandary. She didn't want to say anything to Millie about Luke, but didn't want to hurt her feelings either.

Just then another customer appeared at the desk to pay his check, and Jessica turned to him with relief.

Luke called her at home that evening to tell her he had to go out of town for a few days.

"In fact," he went on, "I'm at the airport now waiting for my flight."

"Where are you off to this time?" she asked, hiding her disappointment.

"Not far. Just Los Angeles."

"Well, I'll miss you."

"Will you really?" He paused for a moment. "Well, then, in that case," he went on, lowering his voice, "I'd better tell you that I've turned down two or three jobs in the past few weeks just so I could be with you. In fact, the only reason I'm going now is because it has to do with a job I'd already begun and really have to finish it up myself."

Jessica's heart soared. Was that the sign she'd been waiting for? Surely it must have cost him a lot to tell her that. And to actually refuse jobs for her sake was almost unthinkable. She knew how much his work meant to him.

"They're calling my flight now," he said hurriedly. "I have to go. See you in a few days."

"Yes," she replied happily. "A few days."

CHAPTER SIX

WHILE Luke was away, the flowers kept coming every few days, and he called her almost every night to tell her how the work was going. Although she was kept busy with her own job and keeping up her apartment, which was now beginning to look like a real home, she missed him more than she ever dreamed she would.

In just the few months she'd known him, he'd become such an important part of her life that his absence from it created an enormous gap.

Then, on her next day off, late in the afternoon, she was just coming out her front door on the way to the Laundromat, when she suddenly came face-to-face with him, just coming up the steps toward her. She stopped short and stared.

"Luke!" she cried. "When did you get back?"

Smiling broadly, he reached out to take the laundry sack from her. "About five minutes ago," he said. "Let's go have some dinner, and I'll tell you all about it."

A rush of pure joy bubbled up within her. "All right," she said happily, falling into step beside him. "But it's only six o'clock. A little early for dinner."

He waved a hand in the air. "Whatever. We can decide that later." He put an arm around her and pulled her to him. "Come on. Let's get in the car."

She was so glad to see him that she would have agreed to go to Mars with him. She got inside the car and waited, her heart singing, her hands clasped tightly in her lap, while he slung her laundry bag in the back seat.

Then he settled himself beside her and put a hand on her face. "I missed you, Jessica," he said softly.

As their eyes met and locked together, she felt as though she were drowning in those deep green pools. The hand moved to the back of her neck, and he leaned toward her, brushing his mouth gently against hers.

"Ah, that's better," he murmured. "I missed that, too. Now," he said, pulling away from her reluctantly and starting the engine. "How does the Paradise sound for dinner?"

"It sounds great."

On the drive she sat close beside him, their thighs just touching, basking in the warmth of his body so close to hers and content just to listen to the sound of his voice as he filled in the details of the job he'd just finished. Jessica felt so relaxed and carefree, for the first time in months.

In fact it was so pleasant to be driving along in the sleek car, the top down, the soft breeze blowing in her face that she didn't realize for some time that they were well on their way out of town, heading east, in the opposite direction from the motel.

"This isn't the way to the Paradise," she said.

"We're not going to the Paradise."

"Oh?"

He shook his head. "Not yet, anyway. Some friends of mine have moved to Europe, and their lease hasn't run out. I'm staying at their beach house. I thought we might go for a swim before dinner."

"Well, yes, but..."

"But me no buts," he said sternly. "I'm staying there, and while I am, the beach is my property."

She wasn't sure she quite liked the way he'd simply made the decision without consulting her, then gone ahead with it without even telling her. But she was too happy just to be with him to make an issue of it.

Soon he pulled up into the curved driveway of a small pink stucco house with a red tile roof. He switched off the engine, then stretched one arm across the back of her headrest and turned to her. "You're awfully quiet," he said in a tone of concern. "Is something bothering you?"

"Not really," she replied, running a hand through her hair to straighten it out where the wind had ruffled it. "I just find it a little unsettling when you make plans that involve me without asking me how I feel about it."

"I see." He paused for a moment, as thought thinking it over, then cocked an eyebrow at her and gave her a smug look. "Not quite what you're used to in your usual circle, is it?"

"No," she snapped, knowing he was baiting her. "As a matter of fact, it isn't. It's what's known as common courtesy, and has nothing to do with money or social position."

He reared his head back slightly, frowning, then gave her a slow smile. "Ah," he murmured. "I see the lady has claws after all."

"When it's necessary," she replied coolly.

"All right," he admitted grudgingly. "You have a point. I'll try to remember that in the future. Now, shall we go for that swim? Or,'' he added hastily, ''would you rather have dinner now?''

She stifled a laugh. ''Oh, as long as we're here, we might as well stay. But thanks for asking, anyway.''

The self-satisfied smirk that now appeared on his face was just like that of a schoolboy who had been patted on the head by the teacher and told he was a good lad. She didn't dare laugh at him, but that small concession went a long way to compensate for his earlier brashness.

''There's only one problem,'' she said. ''I don't have a suit.''

''Oh, that's no problem,'' he said, opening his door. ''I'm sure Sandra has drawers full of them.''

'Sandra?'' she asked, stunned.

He turned back to her. ''Yes, didn't I tell you? She's gone off to join her husband in Brussels. He's in the diplomatic service.''

''I see,'' she said in a tight voice. ''I'm sure you'll miss her.''

He darted her a look. ''And what is that supposed to mean?''

''Well, you have been rather—close—while her husband was away.''

''Listen, I told you once Sandra and I were just friends. At one time we may have been a little more than that, but I have an ironclad rule about married women. Do you find that so hard to believe?''

She searched his face. ''I'm sorry,'' she said at last. ''It's not any of my business anyway.''

''Oh, but it is,'' he replied, his hard look softening. ''What you think is important to me. Now, shall we go?''

He got out and stretched widely. Watching him, the muscles of his shoulders and chest rippling under the thin white shirt, the waistband of the dark trousers settling lower on his slim hips, a sudden jolt of electricity went shooting through her, a sensation she identified immediately as burgeoning desire.

Quickly damping it down, she averted her eyes and climbed out onto the pavement. He came around to join her, casually taking her by the hand and twining his fingers through hers, and they set off for the wide veranda in front of the house.

Inside the cool, dim house, he hesitated for a fraction of a second then turned to her. "You can change in my room. It even has its own private bath."

Instantly alert, she smiled and shook her head. "I don't think so."

"What's wrong?" he drawled. "Afraid I might attack you?"

"Not at all. I just don't think it would be a very good idea. It's a big house. There must be somewhere else I can change."

"Sorry, there's only the one bedroom. It does have its own bath, however." He leaned back against the door, folded his arms across his chest and gave her a lopsided grin. "What's the matter, Jessica? Still afraid of me? Or perhaps yourself?"

Suddenly the pleasure she'd felt at seeing him started to evaporate. She knew quite well what his game was. He'd warned her he'd keep trying, and was obviously prepared to use every trick in the book to get his way.

Damping down her irritation before it could show, she gave him a thoughtful look. "That's an interesting theory," she said calmly. "Did you dream it up all by yourself, or have you been reading Freud?"

"Oh, it's all my own idea," he replied with a wicked grin.

"You know, Luke," she said brusquely. "I think maybe we'd just better forget about the swim altogether."

His face fell instantly. "No," he said, reaching quickly for the door handle. "Let's not. I'm sorry. I just can't seem to resist trying to ruffle those sedate feathers of yours." He thought a moment. "I'll tell you what. I'll wait outside while you change, and you can lock the door."

All of a sudden the whole discussion began to seem pointless, even childish, to her. She also had to admit that there was a grain of truth in his comment about the real source of her fears. There was certainly no danger he would ever force himself on any woman. And she really would enjoy a swim.

"That won't be necessary," she said crisply. "Since it seems to be important to you, I guess there's no reason why I can't change in your bathroom. And I assume it has a lock," she added, giving him a bright smile as she reached inside the laundry bag to retrieve her suit.

His room was pretty much as she'd expected, neat and clean, without a trace of the man's personal life, the bed recently made, fresh towels in the bathroom, where she went to change. On the small counter she did notice a leather shaving kit. It was unzipped, and after locking the door securely behind her, she couldn't resist a peek inside.

There was a shaving brush, a safety razor, shaving soap in a tube. No cologne or after-shave of any kind, and she wondered where the particular masculine scent she associated with Luke came from. It must be the soap, she decided, and somehow that pleased her.

After changing into her suit, a bikini, but a very modest one, she surveyed her reflection in the mirror. It was nothing compared to the far more revealing outfits most women sported on the beach these days, but it *was* a bikini, and *did* reveal a lot of bare flesh. Luckily her breasts were on the small side, firm and high, so that at least there was no embarrassing cleavage to worry about.

However, before going out to face him, she reached for one of the fresh bath towels hanging on the rack beside the sink and draped it around her shoulders. It was large enough to cover her nicely down to mid-thigh, and she'd leave it on until she was ready to go in the water.

She rapped lightly on the door. "Are you decent out there?" she called.

"Yes. Come on out."

If he'd been expecting a half-nude revelation, he was doomed to disappointment, but as his eyes flicked her up and down, there was no sign of it. In fact, the moment she set eyes on him, every trace of nervousness about her own attire fled from her mind.

By any standards the dark bathing trunks he had on were quite conservative, but still, they were *all* he had on, and the sight was decidedly unsettling.

Stripped, he looked even bigger and taller than he did with clothes on, his legs longer, his shoulders broader, his chest wider. He was tautly-muscled, with a flat abdomen, and his chest was smooth, with only a light sprinkling of dark hair running down the middle and disappearing under the trunks.

"I'll just get a towel, then we'll be off," he said, moving past her into the bathroom.

They went through a small living room, also very tidy, onto a paved lanai, then down a short path to the sandy shore. It was still quite warm, the sun shining brightly in a clear blue sky.

Luke paused for a moment, then veered off to the right, heading toward the shade of a nearby palm grove that lined the shore.

He spread his towel out on the sand and turned to her. "Well, how about it? Shall we give the water a try?"

She removed her towel from around her shoulders, laid it down a few feet away from his, then turned around to face him. "Race you to the water," she called, and sped swiftly past him.

He was close on her heels, and by the time she plunged into the surf, a clean clear deep blue-green and warm as bathwater, he'd overtaken her. They struck out together toward a buoy some fifty feet from the shore.

They stayed in the water for an hour or so, until she began to get tired. She turned around and started to swim slowly toward the shore, and in a moment, he came up beside her.

"Had enough?" he called.

"I think so."

"Go ahead, then. Think I'll stay out for a while longer if you don't mind."

She nodded and kept swimming slowly toward the shore. He was like a fish in the water, seemingly inexhaustible, but by the time she reached the beach, she was utterly exhausted, drained of energy, her breath coming in deep gasps. It had been a long time since she'd had that much physical exercise.

She scrunched her way wearily across the fine white sand toward the palm trees, then still out of breath, flopped down on her stomach and closed her eyes.

When she opened them again, it was to a strange half-light. She sat up, blinking, and looked around dazedly. The sun had set. Dusk was falling, and a pale crescent moon had risen in the darkening sky. She must have fallen asleep.

Then her eye fell on Luke. He was stretched out beside her, his head resting against the trunk of a tree, his arms crossed over his chest, his eyes closed. His dark hair, still a little damp, hung loosely over his forehead, and the long black eyelashes any woman would envy rested on the high cheekbones.

She sat there staring at him in the growing dimness, his face cast in shadows now, mesmerized by the sight. It was as though they were all alone in the entire universe, with the surf lapping gently in the background, the palm trees swaying high above in the soft evening breeze.

Then, suddenly, his eyes opened and met hers, holding her spellbound. She couldn't for the life of her look away. They sat there, immobile, eyes locked together, for what seemed like an eternity, until slowly he reached out a hand and laid it on her bare arm, stroking gently.

"Jessica," he said at last in a low voice. "Jess."

The hand on her arm tightened, pulling her toward him. At the same time he inched his body forward, and the next thing she knew his arms had come around her.

Just then, from the private beach next door, the sound of voices broke the stillness, a mother shouting, children's high-pitched voices raised in laughter, and Jessica came abruptly to her senses. She broke out of his embrace, flustered, reached hurriedly for her towel and draped it around her shoulders.

"What the hell is wrong with you?" she heard him explode behind her.

"Not a thing," she replied equably, hoping he wouldn't notice the tremor in her voice. She turned around to face him. "I'm just not interested in that kind of thing. You should know that by now."

He had risen to his feet and was standing looming over her now, glaring down at her, his knuckles resting on his lean hips, his face livid. "You're lying," he ground out between his teeth. "Either that or you're a damned good actress."

She got up and faced him. "I don't know what you're talking about," she replied calmly. "Or is that another one of your Freudian theories?"

"Not at all," he said. Then suddenly he cocked his head to one side and gave her a knowing smile. "Don't forget, I've seen the fire beneath the surface."

She smiled coolly. "I think it's time to leave," she said shortly, and started to move past him.

But she didn't get far. An arm shot out, barring her way, and a large hand gripped her shoulder. A thrill of real fear ran through her and she turned to raise her face to his.

"Stop that, Luke," she said. "You're hurting me."

"Good!" he exclaimed, forcing her around to face him, both hands digging into her shoulders now.

For a long moment he simply stood there gazing down at her, green eyes glittering. Then suddenly he made a noise of disgust deep in his throat and dropped his hands from her.

"If you're really as cold and sexless as you try to make out," he said, "then maybe all those stories I heard about you were true after all."

She stood there staring at him, stunned. "What stories?" she asked at last in a tight voice.

He shrugged. "Oh, you know. How you shut Paul out of your bed once you were married. How you were more interested in your precious social life and spending his money than you ever were in him."

She could hardly believe her ears. So that was the reason for the hostility toward her she'd seen in him when they'd first met! He blamed her for Paul's wild ways, his infidelities.

"And you believed them?" she asked, still staring up at him.

"Yes, I did. Then after getting to know you, I thought maybe they were lies, or at the least highly exaggerated. But the way you've run hot and cold with me makes me wonder if they weren't true after all. I mean, you can't really blame a man for finding his comfort elsewhere when his own wife is an iceberg.''

A sudden surge of pure rage filled Jessica's entire being. A brilliant red haze flashed behind her eyes, blinding her, radiating through her, and before she could even think what she was doing, her arm swept back, the flat of her hand aimed directly at Luke's smug face with all her might.

But before the intended blow could connect, he had reached out to grab her by the arm, forcing it behind her back. She was so angry by now, beside herself with burning mindless fury she didn't even feel the pain.

"And you!" she lashed out, her voice throbbing with fury. "Who do you think you are to pass judgment on me! You, with your redheads, your unmitigated arrogance. You have no right to accuse me of anything. You've been trying to hustle me into bed practically from the moment we met. That's all any woman means to you, another trophy, one more notch on your belt." She stamped her foot. "All this time you've been playing me along, pretending to be Mr. Nice Guy, when all you ever wanted..."

But before she could get another word out, he'd pulled her roughly to him and his mouth came down hard on hers in a grinding, punishing, open-mouthed kiss.

She struggled against him, beating her fists on a chest that felt made of solid steel, even kicking at his shins with her bare feet.

Then, suddenly, she simply let go, went limp in his arms, all the fight drained out of her by the sensations his mouth was arousing in her, insidiously, against her will, but irresistible. Her mind seemed to go blank, and with a little muffled cry, she sank against the long lean body.

An intense heat began to build inside her, and her heart was thudding heavily in her chest. She couldn't think, could scarcely breathe. She was filled with a sense of certainty that this was exactly where she belonged, that whatever happened now was somehow destined, inevitable, and had been from the beginning.

She raised her arms up around his neck, eagerly returning his kiss, joyfully opening her lips to receive his thrusting tongue, raking her fingers through the crisp dark hair.

His hands were moving frantically over her bare back now, and the slight roughness as they slid over her skin only heightened her desire. She'd never felt like this before in the arms of any man, had hardly known such feelings existed. It was her first experience with naked passion and she abandoned herself to it with her whole heart and soul.

He tore his mouth away from hers and moved it to her ear. "Oh, God, Jessica, darling," he breathed, his voice throbbing with emotion. "You'll never know how long I've wanted to hold you like this." He raised his head and gazed down into her eyes. "I'm crazy about you, you know that don't you?"

All she could do was nod mutely, drowning in those emerald eyes, gleaming with desire in the light of the brightening moon. His hands were on her shoulders now, kneading gently. She waited, breathless, ready to give him anything he wanted from her, and when one hand slid with excruciating slowness from her shoulder to the base of her neck, lingering there for a moment, then dropping to cover her breast, she shuddered and closed her eyes.

Then, his palms sliding over her skin, he reached for the straps of her top and pulled them down slowly over her shoulders. The sensation of the cooling evening air on her suddenly bare skin made her shiver a little, and as though in response, he covered her breasts with his hands.

"You're so beautiful, darling," he murmured, his eyes sweeping over her. "Just as I imagined you'd be."

Slowly they sank down upon the sand. The tide had turned and as the water lapped around them, still warm from the heat of the day, he made love to her as she'd never experienced it before, worshipping her body with his hands and mouth, until finally they were joined together, one being.

Later, they went to his room to shower and dress to go back to town for dinner. Love had given Jessica a ravening appetite. She felt absolutely no regret, and not even a twinge of shame at what had happened on the beach. With Luke she had experienced a joy in lovemaking she'd never even dreamed of with Paul, her only other lover. Out there on the beach she had abandoned herself completely to him, shamelessly, in total self-giving surrender.

It was as though her fury, when she'd tried to strike him, unleashed a flood of buried passion from somewhere deep within her, and emotions long dammed up had come rushing to the surface, overwhelming her with their intensity.

When she was dressed she stood at the bathroom door watching him shave. He had on a pair of dark trousers, the belt undone, his upper body bare, lean and hard, the muscles of his strong arms and back working as he scraped the razor over his face.

Unable to resist all that naked tanned flesh, she moved up silently behind him, put her arms around his waist and pressed her lips on the center of his back. When her hands began to snake over his stomach and stop, hovering, at the loose waistband of his trousers, she could feel his muscles rippling under her touch.

He sucked in his breath and stood stock still, catching her eye in the mirror. "Better watch it, lady," he growled.

"Oh?" she said, cocking an eyebrow at him and continuing her exploration.

Slowly he wiped the remaining lather off his face and turned to her, half-shaven. "Now look what you've done," he murmured, reaching out for her. He pressed his mouth in her hair, his breath coming warm and soft in her ear. "Have I created a monster?"

She drew her head back and laughed up at him. "Could be. Are you sorry?"

"Not on your life," he replied with feeling, and began backing her with slow steps in the direction of the bed.

The next several weeks were the happiest of Jessica's life. Her days at work were filled with thoughts of Luke, her nights with his compelling presence. Although they tried to be discreet and keep their affair a secret, they couldn't help running into people they knew when they were together.

There was also no way to hide the glow that suffused her whole being. By then it really didn't matter. They were together, they were in love, and she assumed it was a permanent condition. That's the way things were done in her circle.

She had noticed, however, that Millie was behaving oddly, rather distant and aloof, and giving her strange looks from time to time. But whenever Jessica caught her eye, she'd just smile briefly and look away.

She missed the pleasant relationship she had developed with Millie during the time she'd worked there, the closest thing to a friend she had in Florida, and worried that she might have offended her in some way.

One afternoon, when the luncheon rush had pretty well subsided, she decided to just come right out and ask her. Millie was on her way to the kitchen and as she passed by the cashier's desk, Jessica called out to her.

"Millie. How about a quick cup of coffee?"

Millie darted her a quick sideways glance. "I don't really have time right now," she said, and kept on going.

"Please!" Jessica called after her.

Millie turned around, gazed thoughtfully at her for a moment or two, then nodded abruptly. "All right. Just a quick one."

Jessica poured out two cups and carried them over to a table by the window, and they sat down. Millie sipped her coffee and stared out the window, drumming her fingers on the table, as though anxious to get away.

Jessica hardly knew how to start. Finally she cleared her throat and just plunged in. "Millie, is something wrong?"

"Wrong?"

"I mean, with your children, or something."

"No, nothing's wrong," she mumbled.

"Well, then, have I done something to offend you?"

Millie turned her head sharply and gave Jessica her first direct look in days. "Of course not. What ever gave you that idea?"

Jessica shrugged. "Well, you've been going out of your way to avoid me for several days now, and I have to wonder why. You were always so kind, so friendly, before, that..."

Millie sighed heavily and raised a hand, stopping her. "I'm sorry. I guess I didn't realize I was being so obvious." She frowned down at her cup for a moment, then raised her eyes again. "You want it straight?"

"As straight as you can give it to me," Jessica assured her, and braced herself.

"Well, I know it's none of my business." She smiled. "But that's what they all say when they stick their foot into someone else's affairs. Anyway," she went on in a careful, sober tone, "I hear you've been seen around with Luke Fury."

Jessica stiffened immediately. "Yes," she replied shortly. "What of it?"

"See!" Millie exclaimed, spreading her hands wide. "I've already made you mad."

Jessica sighed. "You're right, of course. I did ask for it, didn't I? All right, go on. I'm listening."

"I like you, kid," Millie said in a low voice. "You've worked hard, when you really didn't have to, minded your own business, kept the customers happy. I just don't want to see you get hurt." She shook her head. "Believe me, I can see the attraction. He's a hard man to resist. But you'll get your heart broken in the end if you count on him for anything."

Jessica frowned. "Are you saying he's deceitful? A liar?"

Millie shook her head vigorously. "No. I'm not saying that at all. I just think you're very vulnerable where a man like Luke is concerned. I don't know how far it's gone between you two, but I'd be very surprised if he made you any promises, any commitment, and I'm just afraid a woman like you would expect something along those lines after things got to a certain point." She reddened. "I'm not prying. I'm just trying to tell you that to pin Luke Fury down, you'd need a signed, sealed and notarized contract."

Throughout this little speech, a gnawing sensation had started up the pit of Jessica's stomach, and with each sentence it grew more disturbing. "I see," she said at last in a small voice. "Well, you might be right, but then you don't really know him the way I do."

"That's true," Millie said with a wry smile. "And believe me, I would never have opened my mouth if you hadn't forced me into it."

Jessica reached out and covered her friend's hand with her own. "I know that, Millie. And I appreciate your honesty, plus the fact that you care. But I *am* a big girl.'' She smiled crookedly. "It may not seem like it to you, but I really can take care of myself.''

Millie rose to her feet. "Well, I've had my say, and now can we please forget it? I still think you'll get burned badly. . .'' She broke off suddenly and smiled. "But, you know, I have to admit, I can't help envying you the experience. He's some man.''

She turned then walked off. When she was gone, Jessica sat there alone for a while, staring blankly out the window at the bright Florida sunshine and telling herself over and over again that Millie was wrong about Luke. She had to be.

For the next few days she continued to see Luke as usual. Her whole world seemed to revolve around him. She was so completely and hopelessly in love with him by now that it was like an addiction she couldn't dream of giving up.

Still, she couldn't quite get that conversation with Millie off her mind. It was true that Luke seemed to be totally unconcerned about the future, in fact, never even mentioned it. Before the talk with Millie, she'd been so happy just to have him in her life that it hadn't bothered her.

Now, however, like a worm in the core of an apple, it began to gnaw at her that he never looked beyond the next day, the next minute, even. It was the way he was, and she accepted that, but her needs had to count for something too. She had to have some kind of understanding about the future.

There wasn't a shadow of a doubt in her mind that he loved her. He told her often enough that he was crazy about her, even that he adored her, and he certainly proved it in a hundred different ways. But there was one word that never passed his lips, the one word she was longing to hear.

Finally she made up her mind she'd have to raise the subject herself. They couldn't just keep drifting on this way, as pleasant as it was. She knew he hated to be pinned down, but surely she could come up with a tactful way, one that wouldn't alarm him.

It was just a few days later that she saw her chance. She had cooked for him that evening, and after dinner they sat side by side on the sofa in her living room, drinking coffee and discussing what they'd each done that day.

Finally, as she'd known he would, he reached out for her and pulled her toward him. "You know, I haven't kissed you once today," he said, smiling down at her and tilting her chin up to face him. "You've become a necessary habit, you know. I can't even go twenty-four hours without the taste of you."

As his lips pressed against hers, one hand slid slowly down to cover her breast, then began to slip inside the loose opening of her blouse. For a moment she was tempted to forget her intention. He had come to wield such tremendous power over her that she could think of nothing but his sheer physical presence dazzling her.

Now, however, steeling herself, she put her hand on his to push it aside, then broke off the kiss and shifted her body, leaving a small distance between them.

"Luke, I think we need to talk."

"Talk?" he said in a puzzled tone. "What about?"

She gave him a direct look. "About us."

He grinned crookedly and reached out for her again. "What's there to talk about?"

"No, Luke!" she said sharply, twisting out of his grasp. "I mean it."

"Well, all right then," he said, leaning back on the couch and crossing his arms over his chest. "Fire away."

His tone was pleasant enough, but she sensed an edge to it, an undertone of suspicion, as though he knew what was coming and was already marshaling his defenses against it.

She searched her mind for a way to begin. "What is it you want out of life, Luke?" she asked finally.

He reared his head back and frowned. "What do you mean?" He seemed genuinely bewildered by the question.

"Surely you must have some long-range plans."

He shook his head. "No," he said quite firmly. "I don't. I learned the hard way that plans, hopes, wishes, whatever you want to call them, have a nasty way of backfiring. I gave all that up long ago. All that matters is right now." Suddenly he grinned.

"What's so funny?"

"Oh, I was just thinking about something I once read, that yesterday was a canceled check and tomorrow an unpaid bill. Only today is cash."

Although she could see some truth in that, it didn't really apply to their situation. She took a deep breath and tried again.

"You know how much I care about you," she began slowly. "You can't possibly doubt that."

"No," he replied. "I can't. I don't."

"And I think you care for me."

"Of course I do. Haven't I told you so often enough?"

"Yes, you have, and I've been very happy with you, happier than I've ever been before. But I have the feeling we're not going anywhere."

He narrowed his eyes at her. "Well, Jess," he said equably. "Just where is it you want to go?"

He sounded puzzled, but in her heart she had the sinking feeling that he knew quite well what she was leading up to and was deliberately avoiding it, playing dumb, making her do all the work.

"Where do you want to go, Luke?" she asked quietly.

"To tell you the truth, I'm perfectly happy with things just the way they are."

Of course, she thought bitterly. Why wouldn't he be? The way they were drifting obviously satisfied him well enough. Yet, as she gazed at him now, the fine features set in a rather hard expression, the green eyes steady, the firm chin lifted slightly, her resolve failed her. Quite simply, she didn't want to lose him.

"All right," she said at last, leaning toward him. "Let's leave it at that then."

His arms came around her, and they sat there quietly for some moments, her head on his shoulder, his hands stroking her hair.

"Jess," he said at last.

She twisted her head to smile up at him. "Yes?"

"You know I want you to be happy, too."

She put a hand on his cheek and gazed into his eyes. "I am happy, Luke. You make me happy."

A look of relief passed over his face. His hold tightened around her, the dark head came down and his mouth claimed hers once again.

And I *am* happy, she assured herself inwardly as she gave herself up to his kiss. It will work itself out in time.

CHAPTER SEVEN

FROM that night on, Jessica sensed a subtle but unmistakable change in their relationship. She couldn't quite put her finger on it, but there seemed to be a definite cooling off on Luke's part.

It was mostly little things. The flowers quit coming, and there were periods of two or three days when she didn't see him or hear from him at all. He was still as ardent and tender as ever in his lovemaking, but at other times he seemed abstracted, as though his mind were a million miles away from her. Worst of all, she felt he was erecting a barrier between them and withholding the part of himself that she loved the most, his vulnerability.

At first she tried to convince herself it was only her imagination, that even the most passionate affairs cooled off in time. Also, by now she was so afraid of losing him that the slightest sign of his withdrawal naturally would alarm her. Luke loved her, she knew he did, even though he shied away from the actual words, and she loved him. That was all that mattered. She kept reminding herself that love meant trusting unconditionally, and she could have cut out her tongue for raising the issue of their future at all.

She should have known better. Luke was a man who had to do things in his own way, his own time and would strenuously resist being pressured into anything he wasn't ready for. She would just have to be patient, that's all.

However, that was more easily said than done.

One night, a few weeks after that conversation, they were just finishing up dinner at their favorite Vietnamese restaurant. Luke had seemed particularly preoccupied all evening. She'd been telling him a story about a heated argument she'd witnessed that day between a nurse and one of the doctors, when she suddenly noticed the glazed look in his eyes, the remote frown on his face, and she stopped in the middle of a sentence.

"Luke!" she teased, smiling. "You haven't heard a word I've said."

"Sorry," he muttered, giving her a startled look. "I'm afraid I must have been woolgathering."

She hesitated a moment, waiting, but when he didn't elaborate, she had to ask. "Is something wrong?"

He shrugged. "No, not wrong exactly. It's just that I've been offered a new job, and it's one I really can't afford to turn down."

She gave him her brightest smile and put a hand over his. "Why should that trouble you?" she asked. "It's your work, after all."

He shook his head. "I don't know. Perhaps it's the thought of leaving you."

"Well, how long will the job last? It can't be forever. I'll still be here when you get back. Where is it?"

"Australia."

Australia! The other ends of the earth! She kept waiting for him to go on, but he only sat there without speaking for some time, his eyes downcast, scowling down at his half-eaten dinner. His hand felt cold in hers, and she had the distinct feeling that there was more to his black mood than the new job. She was just about to question him about it when he raised his eyes to hers again.

"Jessica," he said, his voice grave. Then he smiled and gave her hand a squeeze. "Jessica. Let's get out of here, shall we?"

That night his lovemaking was more passionate than it had ever been before, with a frantic quality in it that almost frightened her. There was no tenderness in the way he held her, kissed her, no whispered endearments, and in the end he possessed her roughly, his body falling heavily on hers.

After he'd fallen asleep, his body turned away from hers, she lay there for a long time, wide-eyed and staring into the darkness, more convinced than ever that something was wrong. Finally, as she drifted off into a troubled sleep, she made up her mind that she'd have to confront him, and make him tell her what was bothering him.

But in the morning he was his old self again, almost as though whatever problem he'd had on his mind had been settled during the night. Sitting across the breakfast table from him she thought he still looked a little worn, the little lines at the corners of his eyes more deeply etched, but the old sparkle that had been missing the night before was back in those green depths.

"When will you be leaving?" she asked.

"I'm not sure." He glanced at his watch. "I'm expecting a call from Sydney this morning."

He rose to his feet and came around the table to stand beside her chair. She looked up at him, wanting to reach out to him, to hold him, to keep him from going, but knowing he had to go, *wanted* to go, was even impatient to get started.

He put a hand on her face and smiled down at her. "I'll call you when I have more details."

She put her hand over his. "Yes. Please do. I don't have to work today, so I'll be right here most of the time."

His head dipped down, and his lips brushed lightly over hers, then came back to linger a little longer, almost as though he was already saying good-bye.

"I'll see you again before you have to leave, won't I?" she asked in sudden alarm.

"Of course," he replied.

As it turned out, she didn't see him again after all. He called her around three o'clock to tell her he had to leave right away.

"Oh, so soon?" she asked, stricken.

"Afraid so. In fact my plane takes off in half an hour."

"I'll get a taxi and come to see you off," she said quickly.

"No," came the firm reply. Then he added in a softer tone, "Don't do that. I'm hitching a ride on a Navy plane and leaving from the base. You know. There'll be a lot of people around."

She was about to insist, to assure him it didn't bother her who saw them together now, but something in his voice stopped her. "All right," she said at last. "I see your point. But you will call me, won't you, to let me know you've arrived safely?"

"Oh, I'll be in touch," he said vaguely. "Now I really must get cracking. I haven't even packed yet."

"Well, you travel light, don't you?"

He laughed. "That I do. Well, good-bye, then, Jess. Got to run now."

"Good-bye, Luke," she said in a small voice, but the line had already gone dead.

Slowly she hung up the receiver, then stood there for a long time staring down at it. It had all happened so fast, she couldn't quite take it in yet. She felt so empty inside. There was no telling when she'd ever see him again.

She gave herself a little shake. There was no point in moping around. She'd known it was going to happen, and he'd sounded so eager on the telephone. There was no mistaking the excitement in his voice, and she envied him the joy he found in his work.

She knew that many women found that same kind of satisfaction in their own careers, but she wasn't made that way. Love had come rather late to her, and totally unexpectedly, but it had taught her an important truth about herself, that her own fulfillment lay in loving, in a home of her own, a husband, perhaps in time children.

Could Luke provide those things for her? Of course he *could*. But *would* he? All she could do was keep on loving him, trusting in the power of that love to guide her. She didn't have any choice. He had become everything to her. Without him there was no life at all.

*   *   *

After he was gone, the days passed with agonizing slowness. She existed only for the time when he would come back to her, and waited eagerly for some word from him.

Every time the telephone rang she would snatch it up, her heart pounding in anticipation, certain it would be Luke. But it never was. She searched through her mail every evening, thinking surely he would have time just to send her a postcard. But she was always disappointed.

She found herself searching through the apartment for some sign of him, some relic, anything, a ticket stub to a film they'd seen together, a stray article of clothing he might have left behind, some indication of his presence in her life.

But there was nothing. He seemed to have vanished without a trace.

She did have a few photographs, candid shots she'd snapped of him on the beach one day, now dog-eared and tattered from constant poring over them. In one she'd caught him by surprise. He was just coming out of the surf, his tall tanned body glistening in the sunlight, his waterlogged dark trunks hanging low on his lean hips.

He was laughing into the camera, one arm raised to shield his eyes from the glare of the sun, the other held out, beckoning to her. The expression on his face was typically Luke, eyes flashing, chin raised, the set of his broad shoulders confident and self-assured.

After she'd snapped the photo he'd come running over the sand toward her, scooped her up in his arms and carried her into the surf, then dumped her unceremoniously into the water. Staring down at it now, reliving that day when she'd been so carefree, so secure and confident in his love, it now seemed unreal, as though it had all happened to someone else, in another lifetime.

Soon it was the middle of August. He'd been gone three weeks, and she hadn't heard one word from him or even about him, and by now she was frantic. He could have been hurt, killed even, and she'd never know about it.

Then one day as she was strolling around the hospital grounds on her lunch break she noticed a group of men standing at the door of Commander Perkins' office. As she came nearer, her eyes flicked over them idly.

Suddenly she stopped in her tracks and stared. One of the men was quite tall, towering over the others, and although his back was toward her, there was no mistaking that thick head of dark hair, that familiar confident stance. It had to be Luke.

With a glad lift to her heart she started walking faster, hoping to catch them up, but by then they had already disappeared into the building. She stopped short, appalled at what she'd been about to do. In another second she would have made a complete fool of herself. It couldn't possibly have been Luke. If he'd come back he would have called her.

By now the long silence had begun to prey on her nerves so that she could hardly function on the job. She was making mistakes in her daily calculations, giving out the wrong change, curt with the customers. One day she even snapped at Millie when she'd asked her, very kindly, if something was wrong.

"Why should anything be wrong?" she retorted.

"Well, the way you've been dragging around the past few weeks I was sure at the very least you were coming down with some dread disease!" Millie shot right back. "Pardon me for being concerned!"

She turned on her heel then and began to stalk off, but before she got far, Jessica had come around the desk and hurried after her, catching her by the arm.

"Oh, Millie, I'm so sorry. Please forgive me."

Millie turned around slowly, folded her arms across her narrow chest and gave Jessica a long penetrating look, still frowning. Then her face softened.

"Sure," she said with an offhand shrug. "It's OK. Something *is* wrong, though, isn't it?" Jessica merely nodded her head. "And," Millie went on, "you don't want to talk about it."

"No," Jessica replied with a vigorous shake of her head.

Millie sighed heavily. "It's got to be a man then," she muttered. "And I think I know which one." She held up a hand. "Oh, don't worry. I won't push. But take my word for it, not one of them is worth this kind of grief."

She turned then and walked away. Jessica stared after her until she disappeared from view, wanting to believe she was wrong, but with the gnawing suspicion that she just might be right.

Finally she decided she'd just have to put her pride in her pocket and go see Commander Perkins. He'd been very kind and helpful to her right from the start, and if anyone on the base would have any news of Luke, it would be him. At least she could satisfy herself that he was still alive.

As luck would have it, the Commander himself showed up in the cafeteria the very next day. It was late in the afternoon, before the dinner rush, and the place was virtually empty. When he came in, he nodded and smiled at Jessica, at her post behind the cashier's desk, then took a table over by the window and opened the large envelope he was carrying.

Before one of the waitresses appeared to serve him, Jessica walked quickly over to his table. "Good afternoon, Commander," she said with a smile.

He half-rose out of his chair, then sat back down. "Why, hello, Mrs. Trent," he said. "I didn't know you waited on tables as part of your duties here."

"Oh, I don't usually, but the waitresses are all busy in the kitchen right now. Can I get you something?"

"No, thanks. I just wanted to get away from the office for a while to read this report."

"Do you mind if I sit down for a moment?"

"No, of course not." He folded his report and put it back in its envelope. "Actually, I've been meaning to speak to you about your work here."

"Nothing wrong, I hope," she said as she seated herself.

"Oh, no. Quite the contrary. Millie tells me you're doing a fine job. I'm just glad it's worked out so well for all concerned. As I'm sure you must have gathered, neither of us were totally convinced it was a good idea.''

''Well, I'm glad I didn't disgrace you. I appreciated the chance very much.'' She hesitated a moment, then cleared her throat. ''Commander, do you recall that when I first came to Pensacola to look into Paul's death, you sent a man named Luke Fury to me to fill me in on the details?''

A look of alarm appeared in the mild brown eyes. ''Oh, yes. I hope he didn't upset you. Luke can be rather blunt.''

''No, he didn't upset me. In fact, he told me exactly what I wanted to know, and as far as I'm concerned that issue is settled.'' She paused again. ''I was just wondering what happened to him. I mean,'' she went on hastily, ''I haven't seen him around the base for quite some time.''

He waved a hand in the air. ''Oh, Luke. He's a rolling stone. You can't pin him down. As far as I know he's still in Chicago.''

''Chicago!'' she exclaimed. She recovered herself just in time and went on in a small voice. ''I—I'd heard he was in Australia.''

''Oh, that job was over some time ago.'' He smiled and shook his head slowly from side to side. ''The man flits around the globe the way other people go to the supermarket. In fact, he was right here in Pensacola briefly about a week ago, just for a flying visit. Then he took off again the next day.''

So it *had* been Luke she'd seen that day, and a cold chill ran down her spine. ''Really?'' she said weakly at last.

"He's quite an amazing person, one of a kind." He leaned toward her with a confidential air. "Has quite a reputation with the ladies, too."

"Yes," she murmured weakly. "So I've heard."

"Then I'm sure you've heard all the gossip, too," he went on in a lower voice.

"Gossip?" she asked. She didn't have the slightest idea what he meant, but her ears perked up immediately.

He chuckled indulgently, even admiringly. "Oh, yes. A girl in every port, from what I hear. That could be why he was so anxious to leave. Couldn't get out of here fast enough."

By now Jessica had heard enough and had to call upon all her training in poise and proper behavior to keep from screaming out loud. Instead, she gave him a tight smile and rose to her feet.

"Well, I guess some men are like that," she commented. "Now, if you'll excuse me, I'd better get back to work."

She walked slowly back to her desk, holding herself stiffly, her shoulders rigid, her arms pressed to her sides, her head a whirl of powerfully conflicting emotion, and feeling chilled to the bone.

Somehow she got through the rest of that day, and it wasn't until she was in the safety of her own apartment that night, the door locked securely behind her, that she let go, throwing herself on the bed and releasing the terrible racking sobs she'd been bottling up ever since her talk with Commander Perkins.

She still couldn't quite take it in. The one fact that loomed above all else was that he *had* been back. It *was* Luke she'd seen that day on the hospital grounds. And he'd made no effort to contact her whatsoever.

It was all over, she thought glumly. No, it had never been, actually. The whole episode had been a dream, a stupid adolescent fantasy she had concocted herself, with no substance behind it.

As the full impact of Luke's treachery sank in, her grief gradually turned to a simmering anger. It had all been an act with him, a well-rehearsed, practiced role he'd been playing. Perhaps he'd been intrigued by her aloof air, challenged by what he conceived as her aristocratic background. Then the minute she'd turned serious on him, he'd disappeared like a flash, with no explanation.

And she'd fallen for it! By now she was so beside herself with a white-hot murderous rage that she could only pace up and down through each room of the tiny apartment, wringing her hands and muttering aloud. She couldn't tell whether it was Luke she wanted to kill, or herself for being taken in by him.

Now, of course, she saw traces of him everywhere. The small table in the kitchen where they'd had so many cozy meals, his favorite record still on the turntable in the living room, the bed they'd made love in. She even, to her horror, came upon a bar of his soap in the bathroom medicine cabinet.

She flung it in the wastebasket. Then her eye fell on the candid photo of Luke on the beach, stuck in the mirror over the sink. She snatched it up and ripped it into tiny pieces, then threw them in the wastebasket, too.

She turned on the cold water, bathed her face, and stared bleakly at her reflection in the mirror. She looked terrible, of course, but what did that matter now?

Finally, exhausted, her anger spent, she dragged herself into the kitchen to make herself a pot of tea. Somehow she had to pick up the pieces of her life and go on. She had no one but herself to blame, and in a way, except for her own foolish expectations, she wasn't even sorry.

Millie had been right after all, not only in her firm belief that Luke would never settle down, but that the experience might be worth it. He was the worst kind of rat, of course, a womanizer, a seducer, a trophy-hunter, an undependable Casanova. But he'd never actually deceived her. He'd been very careful to make no promises.

She had been the worst kind of fool, given herself unreservedly to a man who had no conception of the meaning of love. And she couldn't even blame him. He'd warned her right from the start he had no intention of settling down.

She sat there at the table by the window staring out blankly until the tea grew cold and the sky dark, trying to decide what to do with herself. She would survive the loss of Luke, simply because she'd never actually possessed him. He'd seen to that.

But there was another problem looming in the dark corners of her mind, one she'd done her best to ignore for the past several days. Now she'd have to face it.

She was almost certain she was pregnant, carrying Luke's child, and she hadn't a clue what in the world she was going to do about it.

*   *   *

The first thing, of course, was to confirm her suspicions, and the next morning she made an appointment with a doctor in town.

She couldn't use the facilities at the Naval base, even though she was entitled to them as an employee. Although doctors were sworn to guard their patients' secrets, she couldn't afford to take even the slightest chance.

The woman doctor she chose was brisk but pleasant, and at the end of a thorough examination congratulated her warmly. "Well, Mrs. Trent, I'd say you could look forward to an easy pregnancy and safe birth, with a healthy baby at the end of it, next March, I'd say."

"Thank you, Doctor. That's good to hear."

"Have you told your husband the good news yet?"

"No," she murmured. "He's out of the country on business just now."

"Well, I'm sure he'll be delighted."

Oh, yes, Jessica thought with an inward twist of her stomach, remembering the time Luke had been so annoyed at the antics of the children playing on the beach, his firm determination never to father any offspring of his own when they'd discussed it later.

It had to have happened that first night on the beach, when she'd been so swept away in his embrace that she hadn't even thought about the danger of pregnancy. After that they'd been more careful, but that had only been locking the barn door after the horse got out.

Right now she was too stunned to make any long-range plans. She just knew she had to get out of

Pensacola. Feeling the way he did, Luke must never know. She'd see to that.

That night she called Helen. She had thought it over carefully all day, and although there had never been a moment's doubt in her mind that she wanted the child, she was afraid she wouldn't be able to manage all by herself. She'd have to depend on the Trents for help.

After the usual polite amenities, there was a short silence while Jessica searched for a way to broach the subject.

Finally Helen cleared her throat. "Uh, Jessica, why do I have the feeling that you have something pretty heavy on your mind?"

Jessica had to laugh. "Probably because I do." She took a deep breath. "Well, Helen, to make a long story short, I'm going to have a child."

There was an audible gasp, then, "Why, my dear, I think that's marvelous!" came the quick reply. "I mean, isn't it?"

"It's not what you think."

"What do you mean? You're either pregnant or you're not. No two ways about that!"

"Oh, yes, I'm pregnant, all right. Only Paul is not the father."

There was a long silence this time. Finally, Helen heaved a deep sigh. "Well, that does complicate things, doesn't it?"

"I'd say so, yes," Jessica said dryly. "Anyway," she rushed on, the hard part over now, "I don't think I can manage here on my own, and I was hoping you'd be willing to help me out."

"Of course," was the prompt reply. "What do you need? Money? Shall I come to Florida to be with you? Just name it. An aunt! I'm going to be an aunt! And Father will be thrilled at the idea of having a grandchild."

"Helen!" Jessica broke into the gushing spate. "Didn't you hear what I said? It's not Paul's child!"

"I don't see what difference that makes. Who will ever know? Sure, it'll be born a little late, but who counts these days?"

"A little late!" Jessica exclaimed. "About four months late, to be accurate! More, when you consider Paul and I hadn't even lived together for weeks before his crash."

"Listen, my dear, no one will say a word. They wouldn't dare. Everyone is too frightened of Father, and believe me you won't have to worry about him. I know him. He was terribly broken up over Paul's death, and with his only other child a confirmed old maid, even if he does suspect, he'll never say anything. He'll accept your child as his grandson, no question."

"But it's a lie," Jessica protested.

"Well, we'll cross that bridge when we come to it," Helen replied firmly.

"But please don't tell your father about it yet, Helen. I'm hardly used to the idea myself."

"Fair enough," Helen agreed. "Right now, you need to decide what you want to do. I really think you'd better come home. It's where you belong. We can take care of you—and your baby."

Tears stung behind Jessica's eyes at the kind words. Of course she'd go home. Helen was right. It's where she belonged.

"All right," she said. "It'll take me a week or so to get things wound up down here before I can leave. I'll call you as soon as I have a definite date."

"Good. And, Jessica. Take care of yourself."

Now that her mind was made up, the hardest part seemed to be telling people she was leaving, especially Millie. Since she couldn't reveal the real reason, she was afraid it would seem like an act of cowardice to her, as though she couldn't handle earning her own living and was running back to the money and position she'd left so eagerly just a few months ago.

Still, it had to be done, and quickly. The very next morning then at the usual slack time she asked Millie to have a quiet cup of coffee with her and just blurted it out.

For a few moments Millie didn't say a word. Then, "Why?" she asked quietly.

When Jessica saw the hurt look on her friend's face, with no trace of judgment or accusation, she knew she'd have to tell her the real reason after all. And why not? Maybe Helen was right, that she should just let people assume the child was Paul's.

"Well, I'm pregnant," she said.

Millie's eyes flew open, but in the next her face was wreathed in a bright grin. "That's great, kiddo!" she exclaimed. Then she sobered and searched Jessica's face. "Isn't it?"

"Oh, yes. At least I think it is. But please don't tell anyone about it. Even though I won't be here, it's a little embarrassing, being a pregnant widow."

"Sure, Jessica. If you say so." She paused for a moment, then added, "Not even Luke?"

"Especially not Luke!" Then, afraid she'd said too much, she rushed on. "I don't really want to go back to San Francisco, but I just don't feel I can handle it alone. You know, it wouldn't really be fair to the child."

"Oh, right," Millie assured her hurriedly. "I can understand that. You're just lucky you have a family to help you out."

It wasn't until Millie had congratulated her again and left Jessica sitting alone at the table that the full implications of that last statement dawned on her. Millie hadn't been so lucky. Here she'd been feeling so sorry for herself and her predicament, when Millie *had* done it all by herself. It couldn't have been easy, yet she'd never heard her complain.

If Millie could do it, why couldn't she? For a moment she almost changed her mind about leaving. But only a moment. Millie was made of sterner stuff than she was. With her pampered, sheltered background, she'd just barely managed to support herself, let alone a child.

She rose from the table and slowly made her way back to the desk. She had to leave. She had no other choice.

A week later she was at the airport in Pensacola waiting for her flight. Somehow even now she half-hoped something would come along to stop her.

It had been a hectic week, packing her clothes and what personal belongings she could fit into her suitcases, cleaning out the apartment, arranging to sublet it to a Navy wife whose husband was stationed at the base.

The items she couldn't easily pack, like books and dishes and linens, went into storage along with the few pieces of furniture she'd picked up to replace those provided by the management.

When she'd finished, she walked slowly through the tiny rooms where she'd been so happy. It had looked terribly bare and impersonal, with every trace of her life there obliterated. Nothing of her own had been left, and not, of course, a sign that Luke had ever set foot in it.

Just then her flight was called. She picked up her small carryall and started making her way toward the proper gate.

CHAPTER EIGHT

JESSICA sat in the breakfast room of the Trent mansion staring out the bay window at the morning fog rolling in, pushing around on her plate the scrambled eggs she didn't want and listening idly while Helen and the Senator discussed an upcoming fund-raising ball.

She'd been back for only a week, and was already beginning to fear she'd made a mistake. Just those few months on her own in Florida had shown her what real life could be like. Even without Luke, she missed the more relaxed life-style, the sunshine, the job that had given her her first taste of independence.

"What do you think, Jessica?" she heard Helen say.

She gave a little jump and turned to her sister-in-law, a stocky no-nonsense woman in her early forties who was full of energy. "I'm sorry, Helen. I wasn't listening. Think about what?"

"Whether to have a Hawaiian motif or something more exotic, like Arabian or Oriental. We've just about worked the leis and orchids and hibiscus into the ground."

"Oh, I don't know. Oriental might be nice."

"Well, the planning committee is meeting here this morning at ten o'clock to decide. Will you join us?"

147

"Yes," Jessica agreed. "Of course I will, if you think I'd be of any use. I'm not very good at that kind of thing."

The Senator gave a gruff laugh. "Leave Jessica alone, Helen. Can't you see she's not really acclimated to being home yet?"

Jessica turned to the handsome, silver-haired man with the courteous Old World manners, gave him a grateful smile. To her surprise he'd been so glad to see her that he'd even helped shield her from Helen's determined efforts to involve her in her various projects, and she was grateful. She knew Helen was only trying to distract her, but she couldn't work up the slightest enthusiasm for any of her plans.

She pushed her half-eaten breakfast aside and rose to her feet. "It looks as though the fog might be lifting," she said. "I think I'll take a walk around the garden."

By the time she'd gone to her room to pull on a heavy cardigan and tie a scarf over her head, the fog had begun to lift. In the distance she could even see a patch of the angry gray Pacific, so different from the gentler surf of the Gulf of Mexico. August in San Francisco was a far cry from August in Florida, and she missed the warmth of the brilliant Southern sun.

The Trent house was in an area of wide, winding, tree-shaded streets with large houses, some of them quite imposing mansions. The garden was formal, with neatly-paved paths, lush green lawns and evergreen shrubbery. It took in five acres, the garden shielded from the street by a tall yew hedge, the house set far back, with a winding driveway leading to the front.

Jessica wandered slowly along the flagstone path until she came to the tall brick wall that separated the house from its nearest neighbor. She sat down on the low stone bench beside it, enjoying the solitude and quiet. From here she couldn't even see the house.

She hadn't been sleeping at all well since her return, even though she had her old room, the room she'd shared with Paul during their short time together. Now she laid her head back against the wall and closed her eyes.

Although her plans were not yet definite, she had tentatively decided to stay on with the Trents at least until March. She really had no choice. She had someone else to consider now. Her child. Luke's child, she thought, and the old anguish rose up to haunt her again, the joy of loving him, the pain of losing him.

No! she told herself, fighting back the threatening tears. She would not give into self-pity. She had loved him with her whole being, and he had abandoned her. Yet even in her most bitter moments, she didn't regret the time they'd had together. It was a memory she'd treasure and relive through their child.

Some time later she awoke with a start and glanced down at her watch. It was almost ten o'clock. It wouldn't hurt her to help Helen with her committee. She knew most of the women, and at some point she'd have to get back in circulation again.

At the house there was already a car in the driveway. Part of Helen's planning committee, arriving early, no doubt. It was time to go change into more suitable attire, comb her hair and put on a little makeup. Didn't want to disgrace Helen.

Inside the vast entry hall, she headed for the wide curved staircase. On her way past the main drawing room she glanced inside, but there was no sign of Helen or her friends. She did hear voices coming from the library, however, which was exclusively the Senator's domain. Helen would never trespass on it for one of her committee meetings. Curious, she walked softly over to the open door and peeked inside.

The Senator was there behind his desk, facing her, and as luck would have it caught her eye. "Oh, Jessica," he called, rising from his chair. "Come inside. There's someone here I want you to meet."

As she entered the room she glanced at the man seated across the desk, and at the same moment he turned his head. She stood stock still, rooted to the spot, blinking, hardly able to believe her eyes. It was Luke! It couldn't be, but it was. Then through the buzzing noise in her head she heard the Senator speaking to her.

"Come in, Jessica. I want you to meet Luke Fury, the man who was in charge of the investigation into Paul's crash." He turned to Luke, who had risen to his feet and was gazing at Jessica out of hooded eyes, his expression blank. "This is my daughter-in-law, Jessica," the Senator went on. "Paul's widow."

Luke nodded gravely to her. "Mrs. Trent," he murmured.

Thank God! she thought. At least he had the sense not to reveal they already knew each other, or how well! But what in the world was he doing here? More to the point, how quickly could she get him out?

She had recovered from her shock by now and gave him a cool smile. "How do you do, Mr. Fury?" she said and turned to her father-in-law. "I was just on my way upstairs to change, Father," she said. "I promised Helen I'd help her with the planning committee and they're due to arrive any minute now."

"Of course," the Senator replied. "There will be plenty of time later to talk to Mr. Fury." She smiled again, and walked sedately out into the foyer.

Then, the moment she was out of earshot, she made a mad dash up the stairs to her own room. Closing the door behind her, she leaned back against it, her eyes closed, her heart pounding. What was he doing here? Had he come after her? No, that wasn't possible. He had no way of knowing she was here, probably didn't even know she'd left Pensacola, he'd been so anxious to avoid her.

Could the Senator have sent for him? Perhaps he wasn't satisfied with the official version of Paul's death either, and had decided it would be better to learn the truth than cover it up. But that didn't seem likely. Surely he would have mentioned it to her.

Then from the driveway below came the sound of car doors slamming, high-pitched female voices, and she gave herself a little shake. It was time to change. The committee had arrived!

* * *

During the meeting, Jessica's mind was even more distracted than it usually was during these boring events. She couldn't get Luke's sudden appearance off her mind, or the reason for it. It couldn't have been to see her. What did he want then? And how should she deal with it?

After the meeting, the women stayed for lunch, and didn't start trailing off until past three o'clock. As she and Helen stood in the doorway bidding them good-bye, she noticed that the car that had been parked there earlier, which must have been Luke's, was gone.

Thank God, she breathed. He must have left. She wouldn't have to face him again after all, and the whole thing would be forgotten.

It was the Trent family habit to have drinks in the main drawing room before dinner, which was served at eight o'clock precisely by Mrs. Grimes, the Senator's long-time housekeeper.

Jessica had taken a long nap that afternoon, and at seven forty-five had just finished dressing. Since the Senator was very emphatic about punctuality, she hurried down the stairs, smoothed down the skirt of her dress and ran a hand over her dark hair, then stepped inside the drawing room. She stopped dead in her tracks, however, when she saw that Luke was there, standing beside the Senator who was speaking to Helen.

"Helen, may I introduce Luke Fury, the man I spoke to you about earlier. Luke, this is my daughter, Helen."

Luke took her hand in his. "How do you do, Mrs.—" He broke off, giving her a questioning look.

"Oh, it's *Miss* Trent," Helen gushed. "I'm not married," she added pointedly. "But please, call me Helen."

Luke nodded gravely and slowly withdrew his hand, which Helen seemed clearly reluctant to part with. Jessica stood by, watching. From the way Helen was goggling at him, he'd clearly made another conquest, and a slow anger began to simmer inside her. The man had no shame.

"Good evening, Mrs. Trent," he said, turning to her now. "But may I call you Jessica?" he added smoothly.

Before she could snap out the resounding "No" that had risen to her lips, the Senator's voice boomed out.

"Of course, of course," he assured him. "We don't stand on ceremony here." He turned to Helen. "I've invited Luke to stay here with us for a while, Helen. Would you see to it that the north guest room and bath are ready for him?"

"Of course, Father," Helen said quickly, flashing Luke another brilliant smile. "Right after dinner."

"Good. Now, let's all sit down and have a drink."

He went to the sideboard and poured out freshly-made martinis from a silver pitcher into crystal cocktail glasses, then handed them around. Then he sat down on the couch next to Luke and gave him a paternal pat on the arm.

"Luke has been entertaining me all afternoon with stories of his adventures in the field. Quite harrowing, some of them. Where are you off to next?''

"I haven't quite finished up the job in Chicago,'' Luke replied, leaning back on the couch and crossing one long leg over the other. "Then after that I've been offered a job in Germany that sounds interesting.''

"My,'' Helen commented with something like awe in her voice. "What an exciting life you must lead.''

Luke flashed her his most winning smile. "It suits me.''

"And dangerous, too, I imagine.''

"Oh, it has its moments,'' he replied with a shrug. "But that's part of its appeal.''

Throughout this exchange, Jessica sat with her drink clutched tightly in her hand, her eyes fixed firmly on the portrait of the Senator's dead wife hanging on the wall over Luke's head, trying to make herself invisible. From time to time she was aware of Luke's penetrating green gaze on her, but always managed to avoid any direct eye contact.

"Helen,'' the Senator said, "as I told Jessica this morning, Luke headed the investigation into Paul's crash.''

"Oh, really?'' Helen said. "Then you've worked at the Naval Air Station in Pensacola, too.''

"Yes, quite often,'' was the bland reply.

Helen darted a quick glance at Jessica, but blessedly kept her mouth shut. Jessica steadfastly avoided meeting her eye, but colored deeply at the obvious inference Helen was making. She knew there was no hope of hiding the flush that she felt spreading over her face, and took a quick sip of her martini to cover it up.

Mrs. Grimes appeared in the doorway just then, and with an inner sigh of relief, Jessica set her drink down and rose to her feet. "I think dinner is ready," she said.

Somehow she got through that awful meal, picking at her food and making halfhearted attempts to join in the conversation, which centered almost exclusively on Luke's exploits.

Helen was obviously smitten, hanging on his every word and casting wistful yearning glances in his direction throughout the interminable meal. Finally it was over, and the two men retired to the library for brandy and cigars.

As soon as they were gone, Jessica laid her napkin down and jumped to her feet. "Well, I think I'll make an early night of it. I have some letters to write and..."

"Sit down a minute, Jessica," Helen said, dead serious now. "I want to talk to you."

Jessica sank slowly back down in her chair, dreading what was coming, but seeing no way to avoid it.

"He's the one, isn't he?" Helen said.

"What makes you say that?"

Helen gave a dry laugh. "I may be an inexperienced old maid, but I can still put two and two together and get four. Don't think I didn't notice how careful you were to avoid him, or how he kept looking at you with those hungry green eyes. And when it seemed likely that you must have both been in Pensacola at the same time, it all began to fit."

Jessica stared down at the table, biting her lip, unable to speak. Helen reached across the table, and put a hand on her arm.

"Does he know?" she asked softly. "About the baby?"

Jessica's head jerked up. "No!" she exclaimed. "And he must never find out."

"But why? I mean, doesn't he have a right to know?"

"Luke Fury has no rights at all where I'm concerned," Jessica replied stoutly. "The moment he suspected I might be counting on some kind of future with him, he simply disappeared without a word, and I never heard from him again. Not to mention the fact that he detests children."

Helen gave her a puzzled look. "Then why did he even come here if it wasn't to find you?"

"I have no idea," Jessica replied, rising to her feet again. "And I don't really care."

Jessica made her excuses early that night, as soon as she decently could. The Senator and Helen both seemed so enamored of Luke that they wouldn't miss her, and shortly after the men came back, she retired to her own room, pleading a headache.

Her one thought was to avoid him during his visit, which she prayed fervently would be short. In the meantime she'd stay away as far away from him as possible. Although he'd given her a few meaningful glances, which even Helen had noticed, he didn't seem particularly anxious to talk to her alone either.

There was still the mystery of why he'd shown up in the first place. It surely wasn't for her sake.

As far as she knew, he hadn't even been aware she'd left Pensacola, much less returned to her old home. Could it be he was hoping to achieve some purpose of his own from her father-in-law?

Although the Senator wielded enormous political power, she couldn't imagine what Luke could possibly want from him. He was so self-contained, so independent, and guarded his freedom so fiercely, that she couldn't conceive of him ever obligating himself to anyone by asking a favor, especially a political one.

In her room she went straight to bed. She tried to read for a while, then switched off her light at eleven o'clock, just as she heard the others coming upstairs. She lay there in the darkness for a long time, wide-eyed, staring up at the ceiling, unable to sleep.

In spite of her distress over Luke's unexpected appearance, his arrival had awakened insidious visions of him as she'd known him during their short, ill-fated affair. Luke swimming in the sea, Luke laughing at one of the absurdities he was always finding in daily life, Luke sitting quietly next to her listening to music—and worst of all, Luke hovering over her in the darkness, his naked body pressed against hers, his emerald eyes gleaming down at her...

"No!" she groaned aloud. She must not think about the past. It was over, done with. Oh, why did he have to come back! she agonized, pounding her fist on her pillow and burying her head under the covers.

* * *

She must have slept, because when she opened her eyes again it was pitch dark outside and the clock on the night table read three o'clock. She tried to lull herself back into unconsciousness, but she'd had just enough sleep to make that impossible.

Finally, with a weary sigh, she got out of bed, slipped on a robe and made her way downstairs through the dark and silent house to the kitchen. Maybe a cup of cocoa would help, or a piece of Mrs. Grimes' chocolate cake. She'd been too upset at dinner to eat much, and her stomach was now rumbling ominously.

She had just put the milk on the stove to heat and was about to cut herself a slice of cake when she heard the sound of footsteps coming up behind her. Whirling around, the knife still in her hand, she saw Luke standing in the doorway. He was bare-chested and had obviously just pulled on a pair of worn jeans.

"You going to use that thing on me?" he asked, pointing at the knife.

She gave him a tight smile, determined not to let him get a rise out of her. He had a way of using any emotion, even rage, to suit his own purposes.

"Do you think you deserve it?" she asked lightly.

She turned to finish slicing the cake. The milk was warm by now, so she took down the can of cocoa and stirred some in. It took enormous effort to remain calm, to ignore his potent presence behind her, but somehow she managed to carry her cake and cocoa over to the table, sit down and calmly begin to eat.

"Mind if I join you?" he asked at last.

"No, of course not. I think there's enough cocoa for another cup, and this cake is really delicious."

He pulled out a chair, turned it around, and sat straddling it, his arms resting over the back. "It wasn't cake and cocoa I had in mind," he said gruffly.

"Oh?" she said, with the raise of an eyebrow. "As a matter of fact, I've been wondering just what you did have in mind by turning up here at all. It hardly seems like the decent thing to do."

"I'm afraid I don't know much about your kind of decency," he said shortly. "I'm a roughneck, remember? No polish, no breeding."

"You know that's not what I mean."

"No?" He gave her a dubious look. "Well, to answer your question, I'm here because the Senator asked me to come."

Jessica had to fight to keep the sudden rush of dismay from showing on her face. So, she had nothing to do with his being here! He hadn't even realized she *was* here until he'd seen her that afternoon in the library.

Somehow she managed to swallow the last bite of cake and finish her cocoa. Then she carried her dishes to the sink and after rinsing them out, she dried her hands, tied her robe more tightly around her waist, and turned back to him.

"Well, good-night," she said, moving toward the door. "Make yourself at home. There's beer in the fridge and some cold chicken left over from ..."

As she passed by his chair, he rose up and grabbed her by the arm. "Jessica," he said in a low voice. "We've got to talk. It's true the Senator asked me to come to discuss his son's death, but I really came to see you."

Jessica stood staring down at the floor, her head a whirl of confusion. Just the touch of his hand on her arm over the silk robe was enough to set her pulses racing and make her knees feel like water. She was sorely tempted to believe him. But she didn't dare. She couldn't forget the way he'd dropped out of her life without a word of explanation or farewell. All she could hope for now was to salvage a vestige of the pride he had wounded so wantonly.

She looked up at him. "I really don't think we have anything to say to each other, Luke," she said calmly at last. "And would you please take your hand off my arm?"

He dropped it immediately. "How can you say that?" he growled. "After what we were to each other."

She arched an inquiring eyebrow and gave him a cool glance. "And what was that? What *were* we to each other, really?" She gave a brittle laugh. "After all, when you disappeared without a word I didn't complain. I didn't try to track *you* down. Why must you harass me this way?"

"Harass you!" he exploded. "I've come three thousand miles to say my piece, and I'll be damned if I'm going to back out of it now!" He ran a hand over his tousled hair, scowling in obvious frustration. "Listen," he went on in a calmer voice. "It didn't take me long to realize I was wrong to just vanish that way. I'm sorry. It was not only unfair to you, it was stupid."

He paused then and looked at her, as though waiting for some response, but she remained silent. She would listen, she thought, but she wouldn't help him out.

"I took the job in Australia because—well, because I just needed to get away," he went on at last. "Don't you see? It was wrong to stay away, I know that now, but at the time my feelings—about you, about us—were so confused I didn't know whether I was coming or going. You'd got under my skin like no other woman ever had, and frankly, I couldn't deal with it." He reached out a hand toward her, but she backed away from him.

"Yet Commander Perkins told me you were back from Australia."

"Yes, but only for a day. They needed me for an emergency in Chicago. One day wasn't enough time to get things settled between us. Then when I came back and found you gone, I was frantic. Jess, I know I behaved badly. Won't you let me try to make it up to you?"

Watching him now, listening to him, knowing what it had cost him to come here at all, to tell her these things, Jessica felt a small flicker of hope. Oh, Luke, she agonized inwardly, if only...

If only what? He'd said he'd come here for her, but hadn't uttered one word of love. Besides, it was too late now. Once he found out she was pregnant he'd be out of here like a shot, and she couldn't bear to lose him again. His work meant everything to him. He'd said it himself. While there might be room in his life for her, he'd never accept a child.

No, she thought, steeling herself. Better to send him away now, not knowing, than see the horror on his face if she told him. He must never know.

"But, Luke, there's nothing *to* make up," she said at last. "We had a good time together. No promises were made—on either side. Now you have your life, and I have mine."

"Your life!" he ground out, waving a hand in the air. "Here? In this mausoleum? With all your committees and good works? I thought you were so determined to escape all that."

"Well, I changed my mind," she stated flatly. "Now, if you'll excuse me, I really must go."

"So, it was only a game with you all along," he snarled. "The lady of the manor fooling around with the hired help. Tired of your tame society boys and wanting a little rough trade for a cheap thrill, was that it?"

"No!" she snapped. "That was not it, but you can believe whatever you like. You always have. Now I'm leaving, and if you have any sense of decency at all in you, you'll finish your business with the Senator and just go away."

She started to swish past him. If she didn't get out of there fast, she knew she'd be lost, burst into tears, scream, faint dead away at his feet.

"Not so fast," she heard him mutter, and his hand shot out again to clamp around her arm, barring her way. This time his grip was like steel, his fingers digging into her soft flesh so hard that she couldn't quite stifle a low cry of pain.

"Luke, you're hurting me," she protested.

He twisted her bodily around to face him. "Good!" he bit out. "It's what you want, isn't it?

Play around with toughs like me and what else can you expect?''

She stared up at him, looming over her, an angry flush on his face, a bitter twist to his mouth, his eyes like green slits as they bored into her, and a little thrill of fear clutched at her heart.

The next thing she knew he had pulled her roughly up against his bare chest and his mouth came down, grinding against hers in a long punishing kiss. She began to struggle, but the harder she fought him, the more tightly he held her.

As his tongue pushed past her lips, filling her mouth, the pressure forced her head back, so that all that held her upright was the large strong hand splayed against her back. With his mouth still grinding against hers, his other hand slid down to cover her breast, clutching at it, first one, then the other.

Then, suddenly, his touch gentled, the kiss became less invasive, sweeter, more seductive, and as his lips played with hers, the hand at her breast moved down to fumble with the tie of her robe. When it was undone, and she felt his hand gliding sensuously up over the silky fabric of her thin nightgown, she simply went limp.

The hand slipped inside the low-cut bodice to stroke the bare flesh beneath it, his fingers making circles around each erect peak, an unmistakable indication of a response she couldn't possibly hide.

Under the hypnotic spell of those slow caresses, her head began to spin crazily. She couldn't think. The only reality was the feel of his mouth on hers, the smooth skin of his bare chest under her seeking hands, his heart pounding against hers, his own hard arousal pressing against her thigh.

When his mouth came down to nuzzle at her breast and the hand slid lower, over her abdomen and down to her thighs, a spark of sanity finally pierced through her whirling senses, and she knew that in another second it would be too late. She'd be lost.

Summoning up all her willpower, she twisted out of his arms and took a step away from him, clutching her robe shut, her breath coming in great heaving gasps.

"No!" she cried in a low voice that still throbbed with emotion. "It won't work, Luke. Not anymore."

With a dazed look, he reached out for her again, but she shrank away from him before he could touch her.

"I want you to leave," she said, and although she could still hear the tremor in it, her voice was clear, her tone stern. "Out of this house and out of my life."

She turned then and walked away from him, intensely aware with each step of those emerald eyes burning into her back.

When she reached the foyer, she stopped for a moment to catch her breath, then raced up the stairs to her own room. It wasn't until she had locked the door behind her and flung herself across the bed that the dam burst and the tears began to flow unchecked.

The next day he was gone. She'd slept late, and was just choking down a piece of dry toast and a cup of coffee at nine-thirty when Helen came to tell her. Apparently he'd risen early, said his good-byes to her and the Senator, then just driven off. While Helen related all this, her whole manner was so critical that at the end of it, Jessica felt she had to defend herself.

"You act as though it's my fault," she protested. "That somehow I drove him off."

"Well, didn't you?" Helen plumped herself down on a chair and eyed her critically. "You should have told him about the child."

"Oh, Helen, I already explained about that."

"Well, I still think he has a right to know."

"No. He doesn't. He has no right at all where I'm concerned. You don't seem to understand, Helen. The man just up and left me flat, without a word of explanation."

"But he came back."

"Oh, Helen, you said it yourself. He came here because your father asked him to. If I had anything to do with it at all it was only that he may have hoped to start up with me again on the same old dead-end terms." She shook her head vigorously. "I've had all of that I need. I couldn't take any more of it. Now please, can we just drop the subject?"

Although she continued to try to fit into the Trent life-style, it became clearer to her with each passing day that it just wasn't going to work out.

She was simply bored out of her mind with what seemed more and more like a pointless existence, a constant round of meetings, cocktail parties and luncheons. Just seeing Luke again had brought back all the joys, the deep sense of satisfaction she'd experienced during her stay in Florida.

Finally she made up her mind. She couldn't stay. The baby wasn't due until March. She wouldn't even begin to show for another few months. She wanted to go back to the place where she'd been happiest. With Luke's crammed schedule there was no danger of running into him, nor would she have to work at the base. Now that she had some experience, she could surely get a job at one of the restaurants in Pensacola.

But first she had an unpleasant task to perform. She wanted to start out on a clean slate, with no skeletons in the closet, no lies to cover up. She had to tell the Senator the truth, about her pregnancy and Paul's death.

That very evening, Jessica went to the library door, stood there for a moment, hesitating, then gathered her courage and knocked.

"Come in," the Senator called.

Jessica stepped inside. He was sitting behind his massive desk, piled high with papers. He looked tired, and it dawned on her for the first time what a tremendous responsibility he had in the government of the country, and how capably he filled it.

"Jessica," he said, smiling broadly. "What a nice surprise."

"I hope I'm not interrupting anything important."

"Not at all. Please sit down. Is this just a friendly visit, or do you have something special on your mind?"

"Actually," she said as she took a seat across from him, "there is something I need to discuss with you. Several things, as a matter of fact."

He leaned back in his chair. "Well, fire away."

She took a deep breath. "To begin with, I've made up my mind to go back to Pensacola." When she saw his face fall, she rushed on. "Please try to understand. I do appreciate how welcome you've made me feel here. But I know now the life just isn't for me."

He sighed. "I'm afraid I do understand. In fact, I've seen it coming. You've changed since you've been away. You seem more mature, more sure of yourself." He gave her an encouraging smile. "Now, what's the rest of it?"

There was no easy way. "I'm pregnant," she blurted out.

The pale blue eyes immediately lit up. He came around the desk and beamed. "My dear!" he exclaimed, patting her on the shoulder. "I'm delighted. When Paul died, I reconciled myself to the sad fact that I'd never have a grandchild, and now..." He broke off, his eyes misting.

Jessica gazed up at him, her heart aching for him, what she had to tell him. "It's not Paul's child," she said in a low voice.

He couldn't hide the hurt look in his eyes. He leaned back against the desk, crossed his arms in front of him, and stood brooding down at the floor, chin in hand, for several moments.

Then he gave her a rueful smile. "I don't suppose you intend to tell me who the father is."

She shook her head. "I'm afraid not."

"And I take it there's no question of marriage?"

"None," she said flatly.

The smile broadened. "Am I not even allowed to guess?"

Her face flushed, and she lowered her eyes. "Please don't," she whispered. "It would serve no purpose."

Then she felt his arm come around her, his face close to hers, his brief peck on her cheek. "Jessica, I understand that you feel you must leave. I'm sorry to see you go, but I won't try to change your mind. I just want to assure you that this will always be your home if you want it. You're as much my daughter as Helen, and your child will be my grandchild."

Her eyes filled with tears as she raised her head to meet his tender gaze. She couldn't speak. He meant it, too, every word.

"Thank you," she murmured at last, wiping her damp eyes on the back of her hand and rising to her feet. Then, steeling herself, she gave him a direct look. "And that makes the last thing I have to tell you that much harder."

He stiffened visibly. "And what it that, Jessica?"

"It's about Paul, the way he died."

Immediately the creases on his worn face smoothed out, and he waved a hand in the air. "Oh, that. I've known about that all along. In fact, the reason I asked Fury to come here was to fill me in on the details." He chuckled. "And that's one thing you can count on from Luke Fury, the truth."

"Not always," she murmured, almost inaudibly.

He gave her a sharp look. "I have one last piece of advice to give you, Jessica," he said sternly. "I think you underrate that man, and if I were you I'd tell him what he has a right to know.''

She shook her head sadly. "I can't. You don't understand. After our—affair—he had to leave for a new job. It was the last I saw or heard of him until he showed up here.''

"I see. Did he break a promise to you, then?''

"Well, not exactly. But he certainly implied . . .'' She broke off and bit her lip, realizing suddenly that those implications were almost entirely the product of her own imagination.

"You know him better than I do, of course,'' he went on. "But at my age I've become a fair judge of my fellow creatures, and he certainly didn't strike me as a man to shirk responsibility. I think you should tell him the truth.''

"I can't,'' she said again weakly. "I just can't.''

CHAPTER NINE

IT HARDLY seemed possible, but by the end of the week Jessica found herself back in Pensacola, the late summer sun blazing overhead, the palm trees swaying in the hot breeze, the blue-green surf and fine white sand as beautiful as she remembered them.

She only had to stay two nights in a motel—*not* the Paradise, with its bittersweet memories—but a less expensive one closer to town. There was no way she could get back her old apartment, but there was another one available in the same building, almost an exact duplicate, on the ground floor, and she seized upon it gratefully.

Once she'd got her things out of storage, and a place to live was taken care of, next on her list of priorities was a job. She found one immediately at a small, rather exclusive, French restaurant not far from her apartment, as combination hostess and cashier. In fact, everything was working out so well, that she had to believe it was fate, she really was meant to come back.

Before she actually started work, she called Millie and arranged to have lunch with her on her next day off.

"You're looking great," Millie said as they seated themselves at one of the round tables in the back.

"Being pregnant seems to agree with you. How are you feeling?"

"Oh, I'm disgustingly healthy," Jessica replied with a smile. She reached across the table and gave her friend's hand a squeeze. "Golly, it's good to see you, Millie," she said warmly. "How have you been? How's the job? And how are your children?"

Millie laughed. "Hey, one question at a time. The kids are fine, the job is OK, and I couldn't be better. In fact," she went on, fiddling with her fork and reddening, "I've been seeing someone."

"That's wonderful, Millie!" Jessica said warmly, meaning it. "Anyone I know?"

"Well, as a matter of fact, it's Greg Palmerston."

"*Doctor* Greg Palmerston!" Jessica exclaimed. She could hardly believe it, stuffy old Greg and vibrant Millie. "Is it serious?"

Millie nodded, unable to suppress a grin of pleasure. "He even likes my kids."

"Millie, I couldn't be happier for you. He's a great guy, and very lucky to get a classy lady like you."

"Then you're not upset about it?"

"Who me? Why should I be upset?"

Millie shrugged. "Well, I know you and he went out a couple of times, and I just wondered if you might still be interested. You know, now that you're back in Pensacola..."

"Oh, no," Jessica broke in, shaking her head vigorously. "It was never in the cards for Greg and me." She laughed. "We're probably too much alike. And if you'll remember," she added dryly, "at the time I had other things on my mind."

The waitress came then to take their order, and when she was gone, Millie pursed her lips and looked grave. "Speaking of those other things," she said, "did you ever tell Luke about the baby?"

"No," was the curt response. "That whole affair was doomed from the start, I'm afraid. I was just too dumb to see it."

"Too bad," Millie said. "I thought maybe that was the real reason you came back."

"Absolutely not. And you must swear on the heads of your children never to breathe a word of it to him."

Millie gave her a hurt look. "I said I wouldn't, and you can count on it. Besides, I wouldn't have had the chance even if I'd wanted to. I haven't seen him for weeks, and as far as I know he's still off in some exotic place doing his thing."

"Well, that's a relief. I counted on his not being here when I decided to come back. It's why I didn't ask for my old job back at the hospital cafeteria."

For a moment Millie only stared at her. "Well, if you ask me," she said tartly at last, "you picked a funny way of staying away from him. Maybe you need to ask yourself why you really came back to a place where you were bound to run into him sooner or later." She smiled then to take the sting out of her words. "It's your business, kiddo. But I still think you're making a big mistake. Under all that macho bluster, Luke's a pretty decent guy. He'd want to do the right thing."

It was just two days after her lunch with Millie that Jessica saw Luke himself in the restaurant where she worked.

It was the middle of the afternoon, around two-thirty. She had just arrived to start her evening shift and was on her way from the kitchen to the main dining room when she saw him sitting at a table with a group of other men, some in Naval uniform. They were deep in discussion, and he was turned sideways to her, leaning toward the man at his side.

For a moment all she could do was stare. Then, in the next instant, she swiveled around on her heel and hurried back into the kitchen, the way she'd come. He'd been so engrossed in his conversation that she didn't think he'd seen her, but still the experience was unsettling. She had counted on being able to avoid him, and now she didn't know what to do.

Her first instinct was to quit her job and run back to the Senator's house for sanctuary. It would be bad enough for him to see her at all, but in a few months her condition would be so obvious it would be a disaster.

After about fifteen minutes, she peeked out through the round window set in the kitchen door. The men were just rising from their table, apparently ready to leave, and she breathed a sigh of relief. By the time she ventured cautiously into the dining room to take her station at the cash register, they were gone.

Somehow running across him so unexpectedly had a profound effect on her, unsettling all her preconceived notions. Could Millie have been right? Why indeed had she come running back to Pensacola almost immediately after his visit to the Senator? It did sound pretty foolish. If she really did want to avoid him, this was probably the *last* place she should be.

Millie had also echoed the sentiments of both Helen and her father not only about her obligation to tell him she was carrying his child, but the character of the man himself. Was it merely pride that kept her stubbornly insisting on keeping it from him? And just why had he come to the Senator's house? She hadn't even given him a chance to explain, but the one thing she did clearly recall was that he'd said he cared for her, had come primarily to see her.

She had wildly misjudged the Senator. Instead of the corrupt wielder of power for his own ends she'd always considered him, he had turned out to be the soul of kindness to her, and genuinely moved by the thought of becoming a grandfather, even to a child who bore no trace of his blood.

Perhaps she had misjudged Luke as well. He *had* sought her out. He *did* seem to care something about her. And even if he totally rejected the idea of becoming a father, maybe she did owe him the chance to decide that for himself.

What she needed was some time to think about it, to make up her mind what she really wanted to do.

The very next morning, however, the decision was made for her. She was in the kitchen eating breakfast and browsing idly through the morning newspaper when she suddenly came across a photograph of him in the front section, with an article underneath.

He was standing beside an airplane, his hand on the wing, a broad grin on his face. She was so struck by the photograph that it was some time before she noticed the caption at the top of the article: "Test Pilot Injured in Plane Crash."

Her heart lurched sickeningly, and she quickly scanned the article. According to the reporter, he'd come to Pensacola to look into the near-crash of a Navy plane, and in the course of his investigation had taken it up to test it himself. The article didn't go into the extent of his injuries, only that he'd been rushed to the base hospital in an ambulance. That could mean anything.

She sat there for several moments, her heart pounding, visions of Luke badly burned, crippled for life, perhaps dead, dancing in her head, until finally she couldn't stand it another second. She jumped to her feet, ran to the telephone and called the hospital.

"Base Hospital," came the brusque voice.

"Yes, I'd like to inquire into the condition of one of your patients. His name is Luke Fury."

"One moment." She could hear papers rattling in the background, the usual hospital noises of doctors being paged, gurneys rolling by. "Mr. Fury's condition is listed as critical," the voice said when it came back on the line.

Jessica's heart sank. "What does that mean?"

"Are you a family member?"

"Well, no. Just a friend."

"I'm sorry. We can't give out any detailed information about our patients to anyone but family members."

"But he doesn't *have* any family," she cried, near tears now.

"I'm sorry, it's hospital policy."

"Well, can you tell me who his doctor is?"

"Yes. It's Dr. Palmerston."

Greg! He could tell her what she wanted to know. "Then could I please speak to him? Tell him it's Jessica Trent. He's a friend of mine. No, never mind. I'll come out there myself."

At the hospital she went straight to the Intensive Care Unit on the fourth floor, but was stopped at the desk by an officious nurse who told her in no uncertain terms that Mr. Fury was definitely *not* allowed to have visitors and repeated the fact that information about his condition was given *only* to members of his immediate family.

Just at that moment she saw Greg just leaving one of the rooms, coming her way, and she rushed to meet him. "Greg, how is he?" she asked. "Please tell me the truth."

Greg gave a weary sigh. "It's too soon to tell, Jessica. One leg is pretty badly smashed up, and his vital signs are not at all stable. We won't know the extent of his internal injuries, if any, until we take some tests. But he's a strong healthy man in top physical condition, and he has a fighting chance."

"I see," she replied. "Can I see him?"

He shook his head. "You wouldn't want to, believe me." He took her by the arm and started leading her gently toward the stairs. "We'll know more in a few days. I'll leave your name at the desk as next of kin so that at least they'll let you know how he's doing.''

She left then, her heart heavy. What if she never saw him again? But Greg was right. He was a strong man, a fighter. He'd come out of it all right. He had to! She called the hospital every day only to hear that there was no change in his condition. Then, on the fourth day, she was told that his vital signs had stabilized, the tests showed no internal injuries, and that although it would take his leg some time to heal, he should recover completely in a few months.

"Can he have visitors yet?" she asked.

"Well, yes, as far as the hospital is concerned," came the guarded reply. "I mean, he's out of intensive care and in a private room. But he has specifically requested no visitors, and we have to honor the patient's wishes in the matter.''

We'll just see about that, she thought as she hung up the receiver. He may not want visitors, but he was going to get one whether he liked it or not, come hell or high water.

At the hospital she found out the number of his room and made her way there with a pounding heart. They couldn't station a guard at his door to keep her out, after all, and with his injured leg he couldn't very well throw her out bodily.

Hanging on his door was a large sign with NO VISITORS spelled out in large block letters. Ignoring it, she turned the handle, pushed the door open and stepped inside.

He was lying in bed, his right leg up in traction, but at least he wasn't attached to tubes and monitors, and a lunch tray was on the table beside him. He seemed to be asleep, his head turned toward the window, his arms lying outside the covers.

She tiptoed over to the side of the bed and stood over him. Although he was a little pale under his tan, and the lines around his eyes were more deeply etched, he looked much as usual. He needed a haircut, she noticed, and obviously hadn't shaved that morning, from the looks of the light stubble that darkened his face and chin.

She stood there for several moments, gazing down at him, the steady rise and fall of his breathing, until finally she couldn't resist a moment longer and reached out to smooth the hair back from his forehead.

His eyes flew open, and flicked over her. He blinked, then with a dark scowl, raised his head up off the pillow. "Can't you read?" he growled. "There's a sign on the door to keep people like you out of here." His head fell back on the pillow and he turned his face away from her.

"Aren't you glad to see me?" she asked. She made her tone light, playful, but her heart quailed within her at the blunt note of rejection in his voice.

"No," he muttered. "Just go away, will you?"

She drew up a chair and sat down beside the bed. "I don't think so," she replied perkily. "I came to succor the sick, and you could at least give me a chance to do so."

Slowly he turned to face her again. He didn't say anything for several moments, then finally heaved a weary sigh. "What are you really doing here, Jessica?" he asked in a low voice.

"I told you, I came..."

"No!" he growled. "No more of that nonsense! Just speak your piece and leave."

"All right," she said quietly. "I came because I wanted to see you again, because I behaved badly when you came to San Francisco, because—because I care about you."

There, it was out. She searched his face to see what kind of response he would make to her open declaration, but the sardonic look on his lean face and mocking curl of his lips made her shrink back.

"I see," he said at last. "Now that I'm crippled, you feel it necessary to do your duty, to succor the sick, as you put it, just like a well-bred girl is taught. Well, thanks for the kind thought, but I don't need that brand of charity, especially not from you."

"What are you talking about? You're not crippled. Greg says there's no reason why you won't gain full use of that leg again."

"Well Greg's not the one lying here, is he? Now, if you want to do me a favor, just leave, Jessica. And don't come back." He turned away from her again and closed his eyes.

She knew it was hopeless to argue with him now. When he was stronger she'd try again. She rose to her feet and left.

She called the hospital every day to check on his progress with Greg, but didn't even try to see him again, knowing it would do no good. He continued to improve, and according to Greg there would be no permanent effects from his injury at all, except perhaps a slight limp when the cast came off his leg.

"What worries me," Greg told her, "is that he's convinced he's crippled for life. You know Luke. He's got to be perfect or nothing."

Yes, she knew Luke, and while she waited, she formed a plan that would force him to listen to her.

On the day he was to go home, she dressed carefully in a low-cut yellow sundress with thin straps and nothing else but a pair of sandals. If all else failed, she'd just have to seduce him. Then she rented a car and drove to the hospital, parking in front where the patients were released.

In a few minutes a cab drew up the curb in front of her, and she got out of the car to go speak to the driver. "Who are you here to pick up?" she asked through the open window.

"Fury," came the reply. "Three o'clock sharp, he said."

"Well, we won't need you after all," she said firmly. She took some money out of her purse and handed it to him. "Will that be enough for your trouble?"

"Sure, lady," he said, starting his engine. "Thanks a lot."

Just as he drove off, the glass entrance doors to the hospital opened and a white-coated orderly came wheeling Luke before him, a pair of crutches on his lap. Jessica ran quickly up the path and gave Luke her brightest smile.

"What are you doing here?" he said, frowning up at her.

"I came to drive you home."

"Sorry, I already ordered a taxi."

"And I sent it away." Before he had a chance to argue about it, she turned quickly to the orderly.

"If you'll just help me get him in the car I think we can manage."

"I can manage by myself," Luke barked. "They just insist on these damned wheelchairs so they won't get sued." He set the crutches down on the pavement and raised himself up out of the chair.

He'd obviously been practicing walking with them, and although his progress was slow, he did make it into the car all by himself, disdaining any help from either Jessica or the orderly. When he was seated inside, the crutches propped beside him, she got in the driver's side, started the engine, and drove off.

For a while neither said a word. Jessica was surprised, and intensely gratified, that he hadn't raised a fuss at the way she'd simply taken over. Perhaps now that he was physically stronger, his attitude toward her had softened somewhat.

They'd only gone a few blocks when he broke the silence. "Don't think this means anything, Jessica," he said in a warning tone. "Since you insist on driving me home, I might as well take advantage of it, but that's as far as it goes. From now on I'll handle my own affairs."

"Of course, Luke," she murmured. "Anything you say." She made the turn that led to her apartment.

"Where are you taking me?" he said, instantly alert.

She turned to him and batted her eyelashes at him. "Why, home, of course."

"This isn't the way to the Paradise."

"Oh, I meant my home. I'm going to take care of you while your leg heals. Perhaps even after that."

To her amazement, he didn't say a word, but when she gave him a swift sideways glance it was obvious from the firm set of his jaw, the eyes staring straight ahead, the thunderous forehead, that she was badly mistaken if she thought he was going to give in so easily.

She'd just have to cross that bridge when she came to it. For now, he seemed to be willing enough to let her take him to her place. In spite of the success of her plot to drive him home, she couldn't keep him a prisoner, and no doubt he'd leave the first chance he got, but at least she'd have a chance to talk to him now.

At her apartment, he once again managed the crutches by himself, and she very carefully didn't even offer to help him. Once inside, he looked around for a few minutes, and when he turned to face her she noticed how drawn his face was. The trip home had obviously tired him.

"I think you should lie down for a while, get some rest," she said. "You'll be using my room."

He didn't reply, only nodded and started to make his way slowly down the hall away from her. Jessica stood there watching his awkward progress, everything in her wanting to run and help him, but she stayed put until he'd disappeared into her bedroom.

He slept most of the afternoon, and finally, by six o'clock, she thought he might be hungry. She'd made a large pot of soup during the afternoon, and gone out to buy a fresh loaf of the sourdough bread he liked from the corner bakery.

She knocked lightly on the closed bedroom door, then opened it and poked her head inside. The room was dim, the blinds drawn, and he was sitting up on top of the bed, his back resting against the pillows, his head propped on the headboard. As she entered the room he flicked a swift glance at her, but didn't speak.

"How are you feeling?" she asked. She stepped over to the side of the bed and smiled down at him. "I thought you might be hungry."

For some moments he didn't say anything, just lay there staring up at her fixedly, his eyes searching her face, his expression solemn. "All right, Jessica," he said at last. "Just what did you hope to accomplish by this little scheme of yours?"

"Actually, I just hoped we could talk."

"What about? It seems to me you made your feelings pretty clear the last time we met." He raised himself up on his elbows and gave her a long look. "Come on, Jessica," he said quietly. "The truth. Why are you doing this?"

She looked away, thinking furiously. She couldn't quite come out with the whole story just yet, how much she loved him, the child she was carrying, her hopes for the future. First she needed some sign from him that he cared something about those things too.

She turned back to him and gave him a pleading look. "All right," she said at last. "I'll tell you why. But first will you please explain why you really came to Hillsborough? I know now I was wrong not to listen to you," she added hurriedly when she saw his face close down. "But I had my reasons. After all, you did leave me without a word."

He shook his head, frowning. "I don't know, Jessica. I don't think I can go through all that again."

"Please, Luke," she said. "It's important."

He gave her another long look, then let his head fall back on the pillow and closed his eyes. Several moments passed, and Jessica's heart sank. If he wasn't willing to meet her at least halfway, it was hopeless.

Finally he opened his eyes. "All right," he said in a tight voice. "Since you insist, I'll go over it one last time. I went there to apologize, to explain why I did what I did, to try to make it up to you." His face darkened and he glowered up at her. "Then when you pulled your lady of the manor act on me, I realized it was hopeless. So I got out. Just as you requested."

He stopped short then, and she knew that he wasn't going to say any more. Still, it was enough, more even than she'd hoped for. Now she had to find just the right words to make him understand her position.

"Well, things have changed since then," she began slowly. "*I've* changed. I was wrong about a lot of things. At the time I thought I had good reason for not listening to you, sending you away. You really hurt me, Luke, the way you dropped out of my life without a word of explanation."

"I know that," he bit out, his face darkening. "And I know I was wrong. That's what I wanted to tell you, damn it."

"I understand that now, and I regret what I said then."

He raised himself up to a sitting position and stared at her. "And you came back to Pensacola to tell me that?"

She smiled. "Well, at the time I didn't think so. In fact, when I made the decision to come back, seeing you again was the farthest thing from my mind. But since I've been here, on my own again, I've had a lot of time to think, and I finally realized that deep down I actually came back hoping to see you again." She raised her chin. "I had to give it one more try, and I had to find out how you felt about me, if..." She couldn't say it.

"If what, Jessica?" he prompted, his voice softer now.

She gave him a direct look. "Well, then, if you still cared anything about me."

"Bloody hell, woman!" he exploded. "Why else do you think I tracked you down in San Francisco—or whatever the name of that high and mighty suburb is called? Of course I cared about you. I loved you! I wanted to marry you!" He glanced down at the cast on his leg with an expression of deepest disgust. "But not now."

"Why not now?" she demanded, her hands on her hips, her eyes flashing fire.

"That's a stupid question," he barked angrily. He jabbed a finger at his leg. "I may never walk again."

She stamped her foot in sheer frustration and glared down at him. "Oh! And you call me stupid! It beats me how such a bright man can be so dense." She sank down on the bed beside him. "Luke," she said softly. "What you feel now is only natural after such a traumatic injury. But Greg assures me that with some therapy, you'll be as good as new." She gave him a wry smile. "And then, if I know you, the first thing you'll do is climb back in another airplane."

Although there was a new light of hope sparking in the deep green eyes, the scowl remained darkening his face, and she knew he wasn't entirely convinced yet.

He gave her a quick sideways glance. "Well, it doesn't matter, does it?" he said sullenly. "If you'll recall, you sent me packing the last time we met. Ordered me out of your life in no uncertain terms."

"Oh, that was all an act," she replied airily. "I did that to cover up the real reason I couldn't face you. But now I've changed my mind. You see, you'll have to marry me now."

He raised an eyebrow at her. "And why is that?"

"Well, you're a man of principle and honor, aren't you? So you'll just have to make an honest woman of me."

He gave her a puzzled frown, then his eyes gradually widened in disbelief. "You mean...?" Then he shook his head. "No, you can't mean..."

She nodded. "Yes. I'm going to have a child. Your child."

Still obviously stunned, he turned his head away. "A child," he murmured.

"Oh, Luke!" she cried, leaning over him. "I know you don't like children, but if we love each other, we can make it work. A family doesn't have to interfere with your job, and..."

"Don't like children?" he broke in, turning back to her with a frown. "What ever gave you that idea?"

"Well, that day on the beach you couldn't get away from them fast enough."

"But that was children *en masse*!" he spluttered. "If you recall, I made the point that I liked them fine one at a time." Then he grinned. "Besides that day I was so preoccupied with trying to seduce you, anything that got in the way would have irritated me."

He laid his head back on the pillow and closed his eyes, an almost beatific smile lighting up his face. Watching him, the dear face, the rather shaggy dark hair falling over his forehead, Jessica's heart felt near to bursting with love.

"Then you don't mind?" she asked.

His eyes flew open. "Mind?" He reached out for her, pulled her head down to nestle on his broad shoulder, and began to stroke her hair. "Nothing could please me more," he murmured. "I can give my child the stable home, the father, I never had. Not to mention its mother."

"But what about being tied down?" she asked, still not entirely convinced. "Won't that bother you?"

He shook his head. "Why should it? You want to travel, don't you? If you're right, and I do get the full use of my leg back eventually, then there's no reason why I can't take my wife and children with me on my jobs."

"Children!" she exclaimed, giving him a dubious look.

"Sure. You know. 'A boy for you and a girl for me.' Or maybe more. I do intend to quit roaming the earth one of these days, you know. Then we can settle down, raise our family." He put a hand on her face and gave her a tender look. "Grow old together."

The hand moved under her chin, tilting her head up so that he could look deeply into her eyes. Slowly, their lips met in a kiss of unutterable sweetness. Then gradually, as his mouth lingered on hers, playing, teasing, the heat started building up between them. His hands began to roam over her body, and as one of them slipped inside the bodice of her dress to fondle her breast, she flung her arms around his neck, her fingers raking through the dark hair.

Then, suddenly, as he tried to twist around to press the full length of his body against hers, he suddenly raised his head and made a noise of disgust deep in his throat.

"Drat this damned cast!" he growled. "I can't function properly with it weighing me down."

She raised herself up and gazed down at him. "Oh, I think with a little ingenuity we might be able to manage."

She reached down and slowly, with trembling fingers, began to unbutton his shirt. For a moment he tensed up, then with a slow smile he laid his head back on the pillow and gazed up at her, watching her until the last button was unfastened.

Slowly she spread the shirt open, her fingers trailing against his skin, then bent her head down to press her lips in the center of that broad expanse of bare muscled flesh.

She could hear his quick intake of breath, feel the muscles quiver under her mouth, then grow rigid. When she raised her head again to gaze down at him, the green eyes were glittering, a half-smile playing about his chiseled lips.

"Wanton little baggage, aren't you?" he murmured, reaching out for her and pulling her down so that she lay half on top of him.

"I had a good teacher," she replied, nuzzling his jaw.

"Then why don't you show me what you've learned?" he said, tugging at the straps of her sundress and pulling them down over her shoulders.

As his hands settled on her breasts, she undid the fastening of the dress and wriggled out of it, pulling it down and kicking it toward the foot of the bed. Then she rose up again, his hands still in place, and reached down to unbuckle his belt.

When they had both shed the rest of their clothing, he pulled her down on top of him, their naked bodies pressed together, his arms wrapped around her, his mouth buried in her hair.

"I love you, darling," he murmured in her ear. "I think I always have, and I want to spend the rest of my life with you."

"Oh, Luke," she breathed. "I love you, too. And we will be together, always."

It will be like paradise, she thought, nestling against him, like the Paradise where it all began. Then, as the passion built between them, all thinking ceased, and she gave herself up completely, body and soul, to the man she loved.

LOOK FOR OUR FOUR FABULOUS MEN!

Each month some of today's bestselling authors bring
four new fabulous men to Harlequin American Romance.
Whether they're rebel ranchers, millionaire power brokers
or sexy single dads, they're all gallant princes—and
they're all ready to sweep you into lighthearted fantasies
and contemporary fairy tales where anything is possible
and where all your dreams come true!

You don't even have to make a wish...Harlequin American
Romance will grant your every desire!

Look for Harlequin American Romance wherever Harlequin
books are sold!

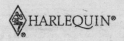

Not The Same Old Story!

 Exciting, emotionally intense romance stories that take readers around the world.

 Vibrant stories of captivating women and irresistible men experiencing the magic of falling in love!

 Bold and adventurous— Temptation is strong women, bad boys, great sex!

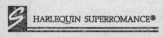 Provocative, passionate, contemporary stories that celebrate life and love.

 Romantic adventure where anything is possible and where dreams come true.

 Heart-stopping, suspenseful adventures that combine the best of romance and mystery.

LOVE & LAUGHTER™ Entertaining and fun, humorous and romantic—stories that capture the lighter side of love.

Harlequin® Historical

If you're a serious fan of historical romance,
then you're in luck!

Harlequin Historicals brings you
stories by bestselling authors, rising new stars
and talented first-timers.

Ruth Langan & Theresa Michaels
Mary McBride & Cheryl St.John
Margaret Moore & Merline Lovelace
Julie Tetel & Nina Beaumont
Susan Amarillas & Ana Seymour
Deborah Simmons & Linda Castle
Cassandra Austin & Emily French
Miranda Jarrett & Suzanne Barclay
DeLoras Scott & Laurie Grant…

You'll never run out of favorites.

Harlequin Historicals…they're too good to miss!

HH-GEN